MAGNETIC COMPASS DEVIATION AND CORRECTION

A

MAGNETIC COMPASS DEVIATION AND CORRECTION

A MANUAL OF THE THEORY OF THE DEVIATIONS
AND MECHANICAL CORRECTION OF MAGNETIC
COMPASSES IN SHIPS

BY

W. DENNE, Extra Master
F.Inst.Nav., Assoc. R.I.N.A.

REVISED BY

Captain A. N. COCKCROFT

GLASGOW
BROWN, SON & FERGUSON, LTD.,
NAUTICAL PUBLISHERS
52 DARNLEY STREET

First Edition	1951
Second Edition	1968
Third Edition	1979

ISBN 0 85174 332 3
© 1979 Brown, Son & Ferguson, Ltd., Glasgow, G41 2SG
Printed and Made in Great Britain

TO MY FRIEND AND WAR-TIME SHIPMATE
LIEUTENANT-COMMANDER HAROLD W. LARSEN,
PH.D., R.N.V.R.

PREFACE

THIS work, in so far as the mathematical theory of deviations is concerned, is based entirely on the Admiralty publication *The Theory of the Deviations of the Magnetic Compass* prepared by the Admiralty Compass Observatory, Slough, a fact which is gratefully acknowledged.

The book has been written in an endeavour to explain as simply as possible all that is involved in the correction, adjustment and maintenance of magnetic compasses on board ships. With the exception of the *Admiralty Manual for the Deviations of the Compass*, now out of print, and the above mentioned work written for the Royal Navy, no other book has been published giving the full mathematical basis on which the practical application is based.

The preface to the Admiralty Manual stated that the theory was intended only for the skilled mathematician. It would appear that this rather frightening comment has hitherto discouraged the majority of seamen, compass adjusters and others from any endeavour to obtain a thorough grasp of the subject, consequently much has had to be learned by rule of thumb.

The fact is, however, that the theory as *presented* in the Admiralty Manual is capable of being understood only by a skilled mathematician. The actual mathematics is comparatively simple and involves no more knowledge than that contained in the first few chapters of a book on elementary trigonometry together with a knowledge of algebra up to and including the use of simple equations.

The methods used in the mechanical correction of the compass are based on theory which is put into practical form only through the manipulation of three fundamental equations. The theory is derived from the fundamental laws relating to magnetic fields and materials. The mathematical manipulation gives the magnetic forces involved in terms of the deviation of the compass which they cause and the Exact Coefficients for any magnetic heading of the ship, but it will not give the deviation explicitly in terms of the Exact Coefficients and the Compass Course, which is what is generally required.

By making certain assumptions and using successive approximations a Fourier's series is obtained which gives the deviation in terms of approximate coefficients and the Compass Course. It also gives the relationships between the exact and approximate co-efficients. The accuracy depends on how many of these approximate coefficients are used. Normally only the first five are considered on the assumption that the compass has been suitably placed in relation to the magnetic fields in the ship. By using the approximate coefficients found by analysis, correctly or approximately, usually approximately, or by methods based on approximate analysis, the compass is initially corrected and later adjusted from time to time as changes in the sub-permanent forces in the ship, or other contingencies, may require. The Heeling Error involves even more approximations.

It is possible, therefore, that a blind use of the first five approximate coefficients for the correction or adjustment of the compass may lead to a false sense of security and perhaps considerable error. This might be especially true in present day ships with so many modern navigational aids of an electrical nature fitted in the vicinity of the compass.

One must also bear in mind that until the ship's electricity supply is made infallible the magnetic compass will remain one of the most important and reliable of all navigational aids.

It is felt that though the seaman in general may not be a skilled mathematician, it is unreasonable to assume that he has no knowledge of mathematics nor that he and others concerned have no interest in the subject when it is required to enhance their professional knowledge. One critic, however, has suggested to the author that the book may be studied very profitably in its present form without a full understanding of the mathematics providing the necessity for its inclusion is understood.

The heart of the book, Chapters VIII to XIV inclusive, deals with the magnetism of the ship, the evaluation of the coefficients and the heeling error. The magnetism is dealt with under three separate chapter headings—preliminary, permanent magnetism, and induced magnetism. The latter chapter explains the conception of the nine rods and the application of their "signs". Here the author has indulged in a certain amount of repetition of description which may offend the pedant but it has been done deliberately to drive the conception home.

Chapter XI explains in detail the method of obtaining the expression involving the exact coefficients. The full mathematical process including all the "steps" is given separately in the next chapter, allowing the reader to omit or reserve the bulk of the mathematics for separate study, if he so desires, without losing any of the arguments leading to the final result. Similarly, the full mathematical process involved in deriving the heeling error expression is kept to the end of that chapter.

The subject matter of subsequent chapters dealing with analysis, theory of mechanical correction and errors of the deflector, in some instances, does involve more advanced mathematics and only the results of these premises have been given. Should it be found in the light of experience that a fuller exposition of these subsidiary subjects would serve a useful purpose, it can be included in a later edition. It has been the aim of the author to include only that which is essential to impart a complete understanding of the main subject, nevertheless it will be found that some hitherto unpublished information is included.

Chapters IV to VII deal with magnetism in general, fundamental facts, the earth's magnetism and magnetic measurements. These chapters are merely intended to form a collection of facts and laws which are required in order to understand the effects of the earth's and the ship's magnetism on the magnetic compass and how the various forces may be measured. They in no way constitute a complete work on the subject. There are many excellent textbooks which include this section of physics, and to these the reader is referred if he requires greater detail. The methods of approach to the subject used in these four chapters are similar to those used in *Text-book of Physics*, by Duncan and Starling, *Intermediate Physics*, by R. A. Houston, and *Magnetism and Electricity*, by S. G. Starling, a fact which is hereby acknowledged.

Chapters II and III are included as a form of revision of the subjects of vectors and trigonometrical ratios. Chapter I is purely introductory giving some advice as to the use of the book with a few remarks on the transposition of terms in algebraic equations. Some worked examples of problems have been included at the end of the book.

My grateful thanks are due to Captain J. H. Quick for his most helpful criticisms and suggestions. to Mr Maurice Disney of the Honourable Company of Master Mariners for editing the book, to Captain O. Fletcher for his criticisms of the mathematics, to the Director and Officers of the Admiralty Compass Observatory from whom the author has obtained, from time to time, much valuable information, to the Ministry of Transport for permission to publish the book and to the Director of the Meteorological Office for permission to include the analysis of the deviations of the S.S. *Weather Recorder*. In addition I would like to record my appreciation of the help given by my wife and also by Captain A. N. Manson with the proof reading of the book.

It should be emphasised that any faults that may be found are entirely due to the author, who would be very grateful for information concerning any errors or omissions that may still remain.

WATFORD 1950.

PREFACE TO THE SECOND EDITION

IN this revised edition one or two obvious errors which had crept into the text of the former edition have been rectified and some minor modifications made to the original text. In response to many requests the author has added the proof of the "slewing of the spheres" and also a section on "pitching error".

EDINBURGH, 1967.   W.D.

PREFACE TO THE THIRD EDITION

ALL c.g.s. units have been converted to S.I. units and various corrections have been made to the text. Some examples relating only to general magnetism have been withdrawn.

CONTENTS

DEFINITIONS OF TERMS, TABLE OF SYMBOLS AND FORMULAE

Aclinic Line. The line on a chart through places where the value of the dip is zero. Synonymous with Magnetic Equator.

Agonic Line. A line on a chart through places of no variation, that is to say, where an undisturbed compass needle will point to geographical north.

Ampere per metre. The unit of magnetic field strength. One ampere per metre is the strength of magnetic field inside a long solenoid wound with n turns of wire per metre of its length, carrying a current I such that the product nI is one ampere-turn per metre.

Coercive Force. The value of the reversed magnetic field required to destroy the remanent or residual magnetism in magnetic material. It is a measure of the coercivity or the tenacity with which magnetism is held in a substance.

Demagnetising Effect. This refers in a particular sense to the field produced by the poles of a magnet in opposition to the field within it.

Equivalent length of a Magnet. The distance between the opposite poles. These are not usually situated at the extremities of the material, and in the case of a bar magnet are considered to be situated at approximately one-twelfth of its length from each end. (See Magnetic Poles.)

Hysteresis. When iron or steel is magnetised by an external magnetic field which is made to vary through a cycle of values, the magnetisation of the iron or steel lags behind the field. This phenomenon is called hysteresis.

Induced Magnetism. A term used to describe magnetism induced in magnetic material of low coercivity and remanence such as magnetically soft iron. The field produced reduces to zero when the magnetising force is removed.

Intensity of Magnetisation. This is given by the magnetic moment divided by the volume of the magnet and is therefore magnetic moment per unit volume.

Inverse Square Law. In all cases where an effect is radially and uniformly distributed with respect to a point, the effect per unit area falls off inversely as the square of the distance from the point.

Isoclinal. A line drawn on a chart through places having the same value of magnetic dip.

Isogonal. A line drawn on a chart through places having the same value of magnetic variation or magnetic declination.

Least Squares. The method of least squares is a method of close approximation for obtaining the most probable value of a quantity from a set of physical measurements. In the case of deviation analysis the principle of least squares assumes that the best values of the coefficients are those which make the sum of the squares of the errors a minimum.

Magnetic Coercivity. The measure of the tenacity with which magnetism is retained by a substance.

Magnetic Declination. The scientific name for Magnetic Variation, *q.v.*

Definition of Terms, etc.—*continued*

Magnetic Dip. The angle measured in a vertical plane between the direction of the earth's magnetic field at a place and the horizontal.

Magnetic Field. The space in which forces of attraction and repulsion due to magnetic effect may be detected.

Magnetic Field Strength. The unit is the ampere per metre. The magnetic field strength at any point in a magnetic field is the force that would be exerted on a magnetic pole of strength one weber placed at that point.

Magnetic Flux. The total number of lines of force or induction crossing a given surface area in a magnetic field is called the magnetic flux. The unit is the weber.

Magnetic Flux Density or Magnetic Induction. The unit is the tesla. Flux density is defined as the number of lines of flux crossing an area of 1 sq. metre, the surface area being considered at right angles to the direction of the field.

Magnetic Inclination. An alternative name for magnetic dip.

Magnetic Moment. The magnetic moment of a magnet is the product of the pole strength and the distance between its poles. It may also be defined as the couple required to maintain the suspended magnet at right angles to a magnetic field of unit strength.

Magnetic Permeability. The ratio of the magnetic induction in the material to the strength of the magnetising field to which it is subjected, permeability of air or vacuum being taken as $4\pi\,10^{-7}$.

Magnetic Pole. The region of a magnet which exhibits magnetic properties from which the greater part of the magnetic flux emerges or at which it enters. In the case of a bar magnet the longer the bar in comparison with its thickness the more nearly do the poles approach the ends of the magnet.

Magnetic Point Pole. A mathematical conception which may be considered as the pole of an infinitely long and infinitely thin bar magnet.

Magnetic Pole Strength. The strength of a magnetic pole is equal to the flux emerging from it. The unit is the weber.

Magnetic Remanence. The magnetic flux (magnetism) remaining in a magnetic substance after the magnetising force has been removed.

Magnetic Screening. See Shielding.

Magnetic Shielding. The tendency of magnetic lines of induction to concentrate on material of high permeability makes it possible to partly screen an area from the effect of a magnetic field by interposing material of high permeability between the source of the field and the area to be shielded.

Magnetic Susceptibility. The ratio of the intensity of magnetisation produced in a substance to the magnetising force or intensity of field to which the material is subjected.

Magnetic Variation. The angle between the vertical plane containing the direction of the earth's field at any place and a vertical plane containing the geographic north and south meridian.

Magnetometer. An instrument for making magnetic measurements.

Moment of Inertia. The moment of inertia of a body about any axis may be defined as the sum of the products of all the elementary masses which make up the whole body and the squares of the perpendicular distances of the elementary masses from the given axis.

Neutral Axis of a Magnet is an axis through it midway between the poles and perpendicular to the axis through the poles. It is sometimes referred to as the Equatorial Axis.

Permanent Magnetism. The magnetism which is retained in magnetic material of high remanence and coercivity for a long period of time. It can be destroyed by heating, by violent physical vibration of the material, by the application of an opposing magnetic force of sufficient strength and to a lesser extent by the demagnetising effect of the field of the magnet itself.

Ratio. The relation or proportion of one quantity to another.

Retentive Magnetism. See Sub-permanent Magnetism.

Sub-permanent Magnetism. A term used with reference to ship's magnetism. It refers to the magnetism induced in magnetic material of medium remanence and coercivity. Sub-permanent magnetism is retained for a shorter or longer period of time depending on the remanence or retentive quality of the material.

Weber. The unit of magnetic flux. It is the flux which, linking a circuit of one turn, produces in it an electro-motive force of one volt as it is reduced to zero at a uniform rate in one second.

TABLE OF SYMBOLS AND THEIR MEANINGS

$\overline{A}$ The Exact Coefficient of constant deviation.

A The Approximate Coefficient of constant deviation.

$\overline{B}$ An Exact Coefficient of semicircular deviation varying as the sine of the course.

B An Approximate Coefficient of semicircular deviation varying as the sine of the course.

B Also used to denote Magnetic Induction.

$\overline{C}$ An Exact Coefficient of semicircular deviation varying as the cosine of the course.

C An Approximate Coefficient of semicircular deviation varying as the cosine of the course.

$\overline{D}$ An Exact Coefficient of quadrantal deviation varying as the sine of twice the course.

D An Approximate Coefficient of quadrantal deviation varying as the sine of twice the course.

$\overline{E}$ An Exact Coefficient of quadrantal deviation varying as the cosine of twice the course.

E An Approximate Coefficient of quadrantal deviation varying as the cosine of twice the course.

F Force between magnetic poles.

H Magnetic Field Strength or Intensity expressed in amperes per metre. In compass work it is taken to refer more particularly to the horizontal component of the earth's total magnetic field.

I Electrically the symbol for Current in amperes. Also the symbol for Moment of Inertia.

J The symbol for Intensity of Magnetisation. Also the Coefficient of semicircular Heeling Error varying as the cosine of the course.

k Magnetic Susceptibility given as a ratio of J/H.

M Magnetic Moment in weber metres per unit field.

P The fore and aft component of the ship's permanent magnetic field at the compass position.

Q The athwartship component of the ship's permanent magnetic field at the compass position.

R The vertical component of the ship's permanent magnetic field at the compass position.

T The period of vibration of an oscillating magnet, *i.e.*, the time in seconds for one complete vibration.

V Sometimes used to indicate the vertical component of the earth's magnetic field at a place.

V Volume.

Table of Symbols and their meanings—*continued*

X	The fore and aft horizontal component of the earth's magnetic field at the compass position.
X'	The fore and aft horizontal component of the total magnetic field at the compass position.
Y	The athwartship horizontal component of the earth's magnetic field at the compass position.
Y'	The athwartship horizontal component of the total magnetic field at the compass position.
Z	The vertical component of the earth's magnetic field.
Z'	The vertical component of the total magnetic field at the compass position.
δ (delta)	Deviation in radians.
δ°	Deviation in degrees.
Δ (delta)	Alternative symbol for deviation.
i	Angle of Heel in radians.
i°	Angle of Heel in degrees.
l	Half the equivalent length of a magnet.
m	Pole strength of a magnet.
R or r	Radius.
ζ (Zeta)	Magnetic Course in degrees.
ζ'	Compass Course in degrees.
θ (Theta)	Angle of Dip in degrees.
λ (Lambda)	The mean ratio of the total horizontal field at the compass position to that of the earth's horizontal field.
λ_2	The ratio λ when the effects of soft iron have been accurately compensated for.
μ (Mu)	The mean ratio of the total vertical field at the compass position to that of the earth's vertical field.
μ_2	The ratio μ when the compass has been accurately adjusted.
μ	Also the symbol for Magnetic Permeability given as the ratio B/H.
Σ (Sigma)	The sum of a number of finite elementary quantities. An approximation, the accuracy of which depends on the number of terms used.
$\tan^{-1}$	An abbreviation meaning "the angle of which the expression following is the tangent".

TABLE OF FORMULAE AND LAWS

$$F = \frac{m_1 m_2}{4\pi\mu_0 d^2}$$

F — Force which each pole exerts on the other in air.

m_1 and m_2 — Strengths of two poles.

d — Distance between the poles.

$$H = \frac{m}{4\pi\mu_0 d^2}$$

H — Magnetic Intensity or Field Strength at distance d from pole strength m.

"End on" Position

$$H = \frac{2Md}{4\pi\mu_0(d^2 - l^2)^2}$$

or approximately

H — Field due to a bar magnet at a point on a line through its poles distance d from its mid point.

$$H = \frac{2M}{4\pi\mu_0 d^3}$$

l — Half equivalent length.

"Broadside on" Position

$$H = \frac{M}{4\pi\mu_0(d^2 + l^2)^{3/2}}$$

or approximately

d — Distance of point on the perpendicular bisector of the magnet from the centre of the magnet.

$$H = \frac{M}{4\pi\mu_0 d^3}$$

$$M = 2ml$$

M — Magnetic Moment of the Magnet.

$$T = 2\pi\sqrt{\frac{I}{MH}}$$

T — Time of one vibration in secs.

I — Moment of Inertia about axis of vibration.

H — Strength of field in which magnet vibrates.

$$\frac{Z}{H} = \tan\theta$$

Z — Vertical component of earth's field.

H — Horizontal component of earth's field.

θ — Angle of Dip.

$$J = \frac{M}{V}$$

J — Intensity of magnetisation of magnet.

V — Volume of magnet.

$$B = B_0 + J$$

B — Magnetic Induction or Flux Density.

Table of Formulae and Laws—*continued*

	B_0	Flux Density of a vacuum.
$\mu = \dfrac{B}{H}$	μ	Magnetic Permeability.
$\mu_0 = \dfrac{B_0}{H}$	μ_0	Magnetic Permeability of a vacuum.
$k = \dfrac{J}{\mu_0 H}$	k	Magnetic Susceptibility.

$\lambda = 1 + \dfrac{a + e}{2}$ $\qquad\qquad$ $\lambda_2 = (1 + e_2)$

$\bar{A} = \dfrac{d - b}{2\lambda}$ $\qquad\qquad$ $A = \bar{A}$

$\bar{B} = \dfrac{1}{\lambda}\left(c\tan\theta + \dfrac{P}{H}\right)$ $\qquad$ $B = \bar{B} - \dfrac{\overline{BD}}{2}$

$\bar{C} = \dfrac{1}{\lambda}\left(f\tan\theta + \dfrac{Q}{H}\right)$ $\qquad$ $C = \bar{C} + \dfrac{\overline{CD}}{2}$

$\bar{D} = \dfrac{a - e}{2\lambda}$ $\qquad\qquad$ $D = \bar{D}$

$\bar{E} = \dfrac{d + b}{2\lambda}$ $\qquad\qquad$ $E = \bar{E}$

$\mu = 1 + k + \dfrac{R}{Z}$ $\qquad\qquad$ $\mu_2 = (1 + e_2)$

$J = \dfrac{1}{\lambda}\left[(e - k)\tan\theta - \dfrac{R}{H}\right].$

$\text{Tan } \delta = \dfrac{\bar{A} + \bar{B}\sin\zeta + \bar{C}\cos\zeta + \bar{D}\sin 2\zeta + \bar{E}\cos 2\zeta}{1 + \bar{B}\cos\zeta - \bar{C}\sin\zeta + \bar{D}\cos 2\zeta - \bar{E}\sin 2\zeta}$

$\text{Sin } \delta = \bar{A} + \bar{B}\sin\zeta' + \bar{C}\cos\zeta' + \bar{D}\sin 2\zeta' + \bar{E}\cos 2\zeta'$

or $\delta° = A° + B°\sin\zeta' + C°\cos\zeta' + D°\sin 2\zeta' + E°\cos 2\zeta'$.

$\text{H.E.} = \dfrac{i}{\lambda}\left[(e - k)\tan\theta - \dfrac{R}{H}\right]\cos\zeta' + i\dfrac{c}{\lambda}\sin^2\zeta' - i\dfrac{g}{\lambda}\cos^2\zeta'$

or approximately

$\text{Heeling Error} = \dfrac{i°}{\lambda}\left[(e - k)\tan\theta - \dfrac{R}{H}\right]\cos\zeta'.$

CHAPTER I

INTRODUCTION

THIS book is written in an attempt to supply all the information that is required for the efficient maintenance and correction of the magnetic compass on board ships.

The methods employed in the mechanical correction of the compass in the Merchant Navy, and for that matter in the Royal Navy, are based on certain assumptions and approximations, the accuracy of the results depending on how far these assumptions are permissible in the actual conditions prevailing.

These methods rely on normal well-established laws relating to magnetic fields and material, but it is not possible by empirical means alone to ascertain the exact qualities and effects embodied in all the magnetic fields in the ship, even though they may be known to exist, nor to forecast all the individual effects, under other conditions than those pertaining to a particular set of experiments, in a suitable form so that a practical correction of the compass may be made.

For instance, a thin soft iron bar, lying fore and aft alongside and to starboard of the compass with its fore end abreast the compass, would by experiment be shown to cause a maximum westerly deviation on North and South magnetic and no deviation on East and West magnetic indicating that the deviation from it will vary as the cosine squared of the magnetic course when the vessel is turned round in azimuth. Such a condition, if present, is not conducive to mechanical correction. It can be shown mathematically, however, that this condition may be split into two, one involving a constant deviation on all headings of the ship which, though not capable of correction, can easily be allowed for, and the other involving a deviation varying as the cosine of twice the course, which can be corrected by slewing the spheres.

Other examples could be quoted, and it is for reasons such as this, together with the fact that approximations are involved, that it is essential to have some conception of the mathematical theory underlying the mechanical correction of the compass if one is to gain the confidence that comes from an understanding of the subject rather than from a superficial knowledge of it.

The author has, as far as is possible, borne in mind the varying degree of knowledge which may be required by those who for one reason or another are interested in the subject. It has also been written in as simple language as possible omitting none but the most obvious of details even to the extent of some repetition. In all cases it is suggested that the book should, initially, be read right through as a paper of technical interest, omitting chapter XII and the mathematics at the end of chapter XIV. By so doing the reader will obtain a mental picture of the whole field covered together with the reasons for the final results and at the same time discover which sections require his particular attention should the complete detail be more than he requires for his more immediate needs.

It is submitted that those teaching the subject will require to know all that the book contains. This also applies to compass adjusters who wish to have a thorough grasp of the subject, bearing in mind that the safety of the ship depends to some extent on their proficiency. It should also be of considerable assistance to those studying for the Extra Master's Certificate, as there is little contained in the book which could not be read into the syllabus, remembering that although the rods b, d, f, and h are for some reason specifically omitted, the candidate is still expected to have a full understanding of the various coefficients which are, after all, only abbreviations for combinations covering all the rods together with the forces P, Q and R.

For the Certificate of Competency as Master a great deal will depend on the time available for study. It would not be possible to cover the whole work in say two months study time ashore, bearing in mind the other subjects to be taken. The minimum required for the certificate is covered by Chapters IV, VI, VIII, IX, X, the *results* obtained in Chapters XI and XIII, pages 98 to 102 of Chapter XIV on heeling error, the rules at the end of Chapter XV, Chapter XVI except the section on errors of the deflector, and Chapter XVII.

It is suggested that by short periods of fairly regular study at sea the whole of the subject could be easily mastered in the course of a few voyages.

Apart from the minimum knowledge required to obtain a Certificate of Competency, the increasing number of navigational aids being fitted in ships in the vicinity of the compass, having magnetic fields of their own which may affect the compass and which may not be symmetrical with reference to its position, make it advisable that this subject should be more easily understood by the Masters and Senior Officers of ships.

In the author's opinion the most tiresome and complicated part of the study is that dealing with heeling error and in particular the effect of the various rods when the ship is heeled. It has been dealt with in full detail in the chapter on heeling error, but if the reader provisionally accepts equation 11a on page 97 he can proceed from that point leaving the earlier sections to be studied later. This also applies to the mathematics at the end of the chapter. Chapter XII may also be reserved for separate study.

Chapter V describes the fundamental facts of magnetism needed in connection with the rest of the work. A fuller exposition, if required, may be found in any text-book on elementary magnetism and electricity.

Chapter VII on magnetic measurements has been included as it is thought that the book would not be complete without some reference to the method of finding the various magnetic values referred to.

Chapters II and III may be considered superfluous by the more mathematically minded, but the trigonometrical relationships at the end of Chapter III will most certainly be required. A knowledge of the signs of the trigonometrical ratios in the consecutive quadrants is also very important as by their use, together with the positive sign for easterly and the negative sign for westerly deviation respectively, all the problems involving deviation may be worked without any "rule of thumb" or aids to memory once a knowledge of the theory has been gained.

Fundamentally, most problems are as simple as the following: "If six herrings cost eighteen pence, how much will eight cost?" To solve this problem one must first know that the cost varies directly as the number of herrings. We first find the cost of one by dividing by six and then multiply by eight, the answer of course being twenty-four pence.

In deviation problems the deviation represents the cost and the factors on which it depends are the herrings. For instance, it will be found in a later chapter that a force P causes a deviation which varies inversely as H and directly as the sine of the course, so that if P causes $6°$ westerly deviation on $N\,30°\,E$ at a place where $H = 16$, we can find out what deviation it will cause on say, $N\,45°\,W$ at a place where $H = 32$. Thus the cost of $030°$ coupled with 16 is $-6°$. To find the cost of one of each of these coupled together we must divide by the sine of $030°$ and also by

$\frac{1}{16}$ (because it varies inversely). The next step is to multiply by the numbers for which we wish to know the cost, that is by sine 315° and $\frac{1}{32}$. Then if $\delta°$ is the deviation required an equation may be written:

$$\delta° = -6 \times \frac{\frac{1}{32}}{\frac{1}{16}} \times \frac{\sin 315°}{\sin 030°}.$$

In Chapter III it will be seen that 315° is in the fourth quadrant and that the sine is negative and equal to $-\sin 45°$. From the ordinary rules of arithmetic we know that when one fraction is to be divided by another we turn the bottom one (denominator) upside down and multiply one by the other. Sin 45° is 0·7 and sin 30° is 0·5, the equation then becomes

$$\delta° = -6 \times \frac{1}{32} \times \frac{16}{1} \times \frac{-0·7}{0·5}, \text{ cancelling we get}$$

$$\delta° = -6 \times \frac{1}{2} \times \frac{-0·7}{0·5}$$

$$\delta° = \frac{-6 \times -0·7}{} , \text{ and as "minus times minus is plus",}$$

then $\quad \delta° = +4·2°$ or say $4\frac{1}{4}°$ E.

It will be noticed that the deviation has changed from westerly to easterly without the use of any rules applicable to force P alone.

During the author's teaching experience he found that many students had difficulty in getting the terms in an equation transposed from one side to another. There are various rules which are normally used such as, shifting a term from one side to the other and changing the sign, cross multiplying, etc. These are all based on one fundamental rule which can always be used if in any doubt: "Whatever is done to one side of an equation must also be done to the other side."

Conversely: "Anything may be done to one side of an equation providing the other side is treated in exactly the same way."

Supposing, for instance, we have an equation in the form:
$\frac{M \cos \theta}{3} = \frac{R - 6}{x - 1}$ where M, θ and R are known quantities and we wish to solve for, or evaluate, x. The equation should therefore be in the form $x =$ "etc.", that is to say, we require the unknown quantity on the left-hand side and the known quantities on the right.

First then, x is not wanted on the right-hand side. We can eliminate that by multiplying $(R - 6)$ by $(x - 1)$ in which case the two $(x - 1)$'s will cancel, but we must also multiply $M \cos \theta$ by $(x - 1)$ in order to treat both sides alike.

Note. We must not multiply by x alone, as the quantity by which $(R - 6)$ is divided is not x but one less than x.

The equation then becomes

$$\frac{(x - 1)\, M \cos \theta}{3} = R - 6.$$

We can eliminate the 3 in the left-hand denominator by multiplying both sides by three and we get

$$(x - 1)M \cos \theta = 3R - 18.$$

If both sides are divided by $M \cos \theta$ the equation becomes

$$x - 1 = \frac{3R - 18}{M \cos \theta}.$$

Add one to both sides and we get

$$x = 1 + \frac{3R - 18}{M \cos \theta}.$$

Here it must be noted that the 1 is not divided by $M \cos \theta$. Alternatively we can write

$$x = 1 + \frac{(3R - 18) \sec \theta}{M},$$

but the part inside the bracket must be solved separately. (See page 17, $\sec \theta = \dfrac{1}{\cos \theta}$.)

CHAPTER II

SPACE AND VECTOR DIAGRAMS
Parallelogram and Triangle of Forces

In order to comprehend the methods used to investigate the magnetic forces which cause deviation of the magnetic compass in ships it is essential to understand the principle and uses of the vector or force diagram.

Before we can deal with the effect of a particular force we must know:

(a) The point at which it is applied.
(b) The direction of the force.
(c) The magnitude of the force.

It is obvious that a line may be drawn from a point indicating the direction in which a force is being applied at that point. If in addition the line representing the direction of the force is made a definite length to represent to scale the magnitude of the force, then the line is called a *vector*.

More than one force may conceivably be acting at a point each in a different direction and of a different magnitude.

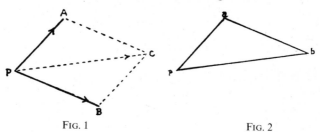

Fig. 1   Fig. 2

Figure 1 represents two forces acting at a point *P*, a force *PA* of 3 kg acting in a north-east direction and a force *PB* of 4 kg acting in an east-south-east direction. If the scale used is 1 cm equals 1 kg force, then *PA* is drawn 3 cms long in a *N* 45° *E* direction and *PB* 4 cms long in a *S* 67½° *E* direction.

From *Fig.* 1 it can be seen that a single force could be substituted of a certain magnitude acting in a direction somewhere between *NE* and *ESE* which would have exactly the same effect as the

6

two forces PA and PB acting together. Such a force is called the *resultant* of the forces PA and PB.

It can be proved that if we complete the parallelogram of which PA and PB are adjacent sides, then the diagonal PC (*Fig.* 1) represents the resultant force in direction and magnitude. Thus a single force of 5·85 kg acting in a $N\,84\frac{1}{4}°\,E$ direction would have the same effect as that obtained by the two forces PA and PB.

Referring again to *Fig.* 1, AC is equal in length and parallel to PB. Hence, if we draw the vector PB from A instead of P and complete the triangle we then get *Fig.* 2 in which $pa = PA$ in direction and length, $ab = AC$ in direction and length and $pb = PC$ in direction and length. The diagram pab is called the triangle of forces or *vector diagram* of the forces PA and PB, giving the magnitude and direction of the two forces and the magnitude and direction of the resultant, the latter (pb in *Fig.* 2) is often referred to as the *vector sum* of pa and ab.

By adding the vectors, as illustrated in the above example of the two forces, the resultant of several forces, all acting at one point, may be found. See *Fig.* 3 and *Fig.* 4.

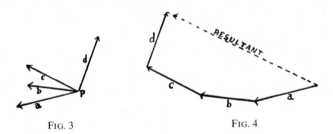

FIG. 3   FIG. 4

It should be noted that if a force were applied at the point P equal in magnitude to the resultant but in exactly the opposite direction, then the whole system would be in equilibrium. Such a force is called the *equilibrant*.

Conversely to the foregoing, it is possible that having a single force of known magnitude acting at a point in a particular direction, we might prefer to substitute two or more forces acting in other directions which would have exactly the same effect as the single force. In other words, we should require to know the value of the forces of which the single force was the resultant. In order to do this we have two alternatives:

(1) To decide on the magnitude of the forces we are to use and then find the directions in which they should respectively act, or

(2) To decide on the directions in which these forces are to act and then find the magnitude of the forces required.

It is the second of these two alternatives that is used in the approach to most solutions of problems involving the cause and correction of deviations of the magnetic compass.

Let a force z of 5 kg be acting in a $N\ 37°\ E$ direction at a point P (*Fig. 5*). It is required to substitute two forces x and y acting in a Northerly and in an Easterly direction respectively.

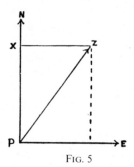

FIG. 5

Let PZ represent the force z in magnitude and direction.

Let PN and PE represent the direction of the forces x and y respectively.

Through Z draw a line parallel to PE cutting PN in X.

Then PX represents the magnitude of force x and XZ the magnitude of the force y.

PZX is thus the vector diagram containing the required forces x and y with the force z as the resultant, from which it will be found that $x = 4$ kg and $y = 3$ kg.

It will be found subsequently that the earth's magnetic force acts at an angle to the horizontal at most points on the earth's surface. It is necessary that the direction and magnitude of this force be known. The direction can be accurately measured as the angle at which the force dips below the horizontal plane. Obtaining the magnitude of the force is a more difficult problem, but it has been found that it is a comparatively simple matter to measure the effect of the force in a horizontal direction, or to find what is generally known as the *horizontal component* of the total force.

Obviously there must be at least one other component force, and as the total force is acting in a direction between the horizontal and the vertical, it is only logical to use the effect of the force in a vertical direction as a second component. This is known as the *vertical component* of the total force.

Assuming, then, as an example that the direction of the earth's magnetic force at a certain place dips down below the horizontal at an angle of 67°, and that the horizontal component is found to be 18 units, we can by using the principles discussed above find the magnitude of the total force and, if required, the value of the vertical component.

Let PT (*Fig.* 6) represent the direction of the earth's total force.

From P draw PH in a horizontal direction 18 units in length.

Then angle $HPT = 67°$.

From H drop HT in a vertical direction to cut PT in T.

Then the length PT represents the magnitude of the earth's total force, and will be found to measure 46 units. Also HT represents the magnitude of the earth's vertical component, and will

FIG. 6

be found to measure 42 units. The triangle PHT is the vector diagram or triangle of forces for the forces concerned. The above results could have been obtained by calculation using the trigonometrical ratios.

Similarly, a local magnetic force in a ship may be acting in a direction neither fore and aft or athwartships nor horizontal or vertical, as for instance a force acting through the compass position in a direction parallel with a line drawn from a point on the port side of the fore deck to a point in the starboard after bilge. In order to assess the magnitude of such a force it is necessary, for practical reasons, to consider first its horizontal and vertical components. The former would be acting in a horizontal direction through the compass position from the port bow to the starboard quarter, while the latter would be acting vertically through the compass position. It will be seen later that such a vertical force can be readily assessed, this however does not apply to the horizontal component. For practical reasons again, the horizontal component must itself be divided into two components, one in a fore and aft direction and the other in an athwartship direction. Thus in order to measure the effects of such a force in a ship it is first necessary to measure the effects of the fore and aft and athwartship components and then by means of the vector diagram the resultant or total effect of the horizontal component. Then with this component and the vertical component, a second vector diagram could be obtained giving a final resultant or the effect of the actual or total force at the compass position.

This may at first appear very complicated, but in practice we concern ourselves solely with the fore and aft horizontal component, the athwartship horizontal component, and the vertical component of any magnetic forces acting at the compass position. We are not particularly concerned with either the magnitude or direction of the total force.

The effect of a magnetic force at the compass position is to cause deviation. The effect of the three components just mentioned can be measured in terms of the deviation caused. In addition, no matter what may be the actual direction of any such local magnetic force, its three components are always acting along the same directions and are always at right angles to each other each to each. Therefore by inserting correcting forces in the direction of each component, having equal but opposite effect, we can nullify the deviation each is causing. We thus have a method of compensating for deviations caused by the ship's magnetism whereby the correctors are always placed in the same direction with reference to the compass no matter what the direction of the disturbing force may be.

Secondly, the fact that the component forces are always at right angles to one another allows simple trigonometrical solutions to be made.

The student should also make himself familiar with the idea of positive and negative directions and positive and negative forces.

A force may for convenience be considered positive if acting in one direction and negative if acting in the opposite direction; or simply one direction may be considered positive and the opposite direction negative.

Again, it is sometimes convenient to consider a force which is actually acting in one direction to be acting in exactly the opposite direction. It then becomes a negative force acting in the latter direction.

CHAPTER III

TRIGONOMETRICAL RATIOS

IN dealing with the deviations of the magnetic compass, their cause and correction, it is essential to have a thorough understanding of the trigonometrical ratios of the angles involved, in particular of the sine, cosine, and tangent.

The angle under consideration is always considered to be one of, or related to one of the interior angles of a right angled triangle, the ratios being in fact simply the ratio of one side of the triangle to that of another in each case. In the case of the sine or the cosine, the ratio is given in terms of the hypotenuse and in the case of the tangent as the ratio of one of the sides containing the right angle in terms of the other.

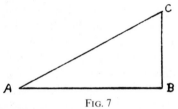

FIG. 7

Thus in the triangle ABC right angled at B (*Fig. 7*)

The sine of angle A is $\dfrac{CB}{AC}$, *i.e.*, the opposite side over the hypotenuse.

The cosine of angle A is $\dfrac{AB}{AC}$, *i.e.*, the adjacent side over the hypotenuse.

The tangent of angle A is $\dfrac{CB}{AB}$, *i.e.*, the opposite side over the adjacent side.

If angle A is made 30° and AC one metre or other unit in length, it will be found that CB will measure 0·5 metres or 0·5 units exactly. The sine of 30° is therefore $\dfrac{0·5}{1} = 0·5$. In other words the ratio of the side CB to the hypotenuse is 0·5, or CB is half the length of the hypotenuse when the angle concerned is 30°.

11

Similarly, under the same conditions it will be found that the side AB measures 0·866 units nearly, hence the cosine of 30° is $\frac{0·866}{1} = 0·866$ and the ratio of the side AB to the hypotenuse is therefore 0·866 to three decimal places. Again, the tangent of 30° is the ratio of the opposite side to the adjacent side, *i.e.*, $\frac{0·5}{0·866} = 0·577$ to three decimal places.

The log sine of 30° is of course the log of 0·5, *i.e.*, $\bar{1}·69897$ (or 9·69897) to five decimal places. Similarly, the log cosine of 30° is the log of 0·866 equal to $\bar{1}·93752$ (or 9·93752), and the log tangent of 30° is the log of 0·577, equal to $\bar{1}·76118$ (or 9·76118) to five decimal places respectively.

The student might check these results using his Tables of Natural Ratios and Logarithms against the table of Log Ratios.

The above relationships apply equally to the exterior angles of right-angled triangles and to angles of any size or measurement except that some of the ratios will have negative values when the angle concerned is greater than 90°. It is with this aspect that this chapter is chiefly concerned, as the published tables of sines, cosines and tangents give these values for angles from 0° to 90° only, or for an interior angle of a right-angled triangle, whereas we often require the ratios of angles with values greater than 90°.

It is necessary here to call to mind the method of plotting graphs, the seaman will be conversant with Displacement Curves involving the plotting of Displacement against Draught, or Statical Stability Curves involving the plotting of Righting Levers (*GZ*'s) against Angles of Heel. In the former case, the curve of Displacement will always be contained in the positive quadrant, as one can hardly conceive either a negative draught or a negative displacement, but in the case of stability curves the righting lever may in certain circumstances be negative, in which case it is conventional to draw the negative part of the curve below the base line. Here again, although the righting lever may be negative, the angle of heel is always considered positive, hence in either case the curve is always drawn toward the right with the point of origin and vertical scale at the left-hand side of the sheet.

In order to plot a curve in which either quantity may be positive or negative, the point of origin or zero of both scales is placed at the centre of the sheet. The horizontal scale is drawn to the left as well as to the right of the point of origin and graduated from zero in both directions, values to the right being considered positive and those to the left negative. Similarly, the vertical scale is drawn down as well as up from the point of origin and graduated from zero in both directions, the values above the base line being considered positive and those below the line negative. The two scales, horizontal and vertical, intersecting at the zero of both scales, are called the *Axes of Reference*.

In *Fig.* 8, *XOX'* and *YOY'* represent such horizontal and vertical axes respectively. *O* is the point of origin or zero of the scales.

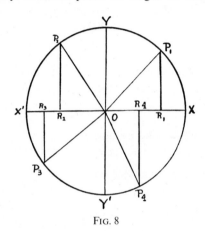

FIG. 8

The direction *OX*, *i.e.*, to the right, is positive, and the direction *OX'*, *i.e.*, to the left, is negative. The direction *OY*, *i.e.*, above the horizontal, is positive, and the direction *OY'*, *i.e.*, below the horizontal, is negative.

Take a radius of any unit length and with centre *O* describe a circle cutting the horizontal and vertical axes in *X* and *X'* and *Y* and *Y'* respectively. Then any radius of the circle *XYX'Y'* will have unit length.

The quadrants *XOY*, *X'OY*, *X'OY'* and *XOY'* are called the first, second, third and fourth quadrants respectively.

In the first quadrant both the *X* co-ordinate and the *Y* co-ordinate will be positive.

In the second quadrant the *X* co-ordinate is negative but the *Y* co-ordinate is still positive.

In the third quadrant both the *X* and *Y* co-ordinates are negative.

In the fourth quadrant the *X* co-ordinate is positive but the *Y* co-ordinate is negative.

Imagine a radius of the circle *XYX'Y'* to be coincident with

OX making an angle of zero degrees with OX at X. Now let this radius revolve anti-clockwise about O until it reaches a point OP_1 *in the first quadrant forming the angle XOP_1 at O.*

From OP_1 draw a perpendicular to OX cutting OX in R_1 and completing the right-angled triangle P_1OR_1.

Then   sine $XOP_1 = \dfrac{P_1R_1}{OP_1} = \dfrac{P_1R_1}{1} = P_1R_1$ and P_1R_1 is positive.

Cosine $XOP_1 = \dfrac{OR_1}{OP_1} = \dfrac{OR_1}{1} = OR_1$ and OR_1 is positive.

Tangent $XOP_1 = \dfrac{P_1R_1}{OR_1} = \dfrac{\sin XOP_1}{\cos XOP_1}$ and is positive.

Let the radius now continue to revolve anti-clockwise to position OP_2 in the second quadrant forming the angle XOP_2 greater than $90°$ but less than $180°$.

From P_2 draw a perpendicular to OX' cutting OX' in R_2 and completing the right-angled triangle P_2OR_2.

The angle XOP_2 is the exterior angle of the triangle at O.

Sine $XOP_2 = P_2R_2$ and is positive.

Cosine $XOP_2 = OR_2$ is to the left and therefore negative.

Tangent $XOP_2 = \dfrac{\sin}{-\cos}$, *i.e.,* $\dfrac{\text{positive}}{\text{negative}}$ and therefore negative.

If we now refer to the right-angled triangle P_2R_2O the interior angle at O is less than $90°$, and must therefore be considered in the first quadrant.

The hypotenuse is equal to unity and is always positive.

Sine $P_2OR_2 = P_2R_2$

Cosine $P_2OR_2 = OR_2$

Tangent $P_2OR_2 = \dfrac{\sin}{\cos}$ and all are positive.

But $P_2OR_2 = (180 - XOP_2)$.

Hence   sine $XOP_2 = +\sin(180 - XOP_2)$

cosine $XOP_2 = -\cos(180 - XOP_2)$

tangent $XOP_2 = -\tan(180 - XOP_2)$.

Next let the radius continue to revolve further, still anti-clockwise, to position OP_3 in the third quadrant forming the reflex angle XOP_3

greater than 180° but less than 270°. From P_3 draw a perpendicular to OX' cutting OX' in R_3 and completing the right-angled triangle P_3OR_3.

Then sine reflex $XOP_3 = P_3R_3$ (below the horizontal and therefore negative).

Cosine reflex $XOP_3 = OR_3$ (to the left and therefore negative).

Tangent reflex $XOP_3 = \dfrac{-\sin}{-\cos} = \dfrac{\text{negative}}{\text{negative}}$ and is therefore positive.

By the same reasoning used for the second quadrant, in right-angled triangle P_3OR_3

Sine $P_3OR_3 = P_3R_3$

Cosine $P_3OR_3 = OR_3$

Tangent $P_3OR_3 = \dfrac{\sin P_3OR_3}{\cos P_3OR_3}$.

But $P_3OR_3 = (XOP_3 - 180)$.

Hence   sine $XOP_3 = -\sin(XOP_3 - 180)$

cosine $XOP_3 = -\cos(XOP_3 - 180)$

tangent $XOP_3 = +\tan(XOP_3 - 180)$.

Continuing, let the radius revolve still farther until it reaches position OP_4 in the fourth quadrant forming the reflex angle XOP_4 greater than 270° but less than 360°. From P_4 draw a perpendicular to OX cutting OX in R_4 and completing the right-angled triangle P_4R_4O.

Sine reflex $XOP_4 = P_4R_4$ below the horizontal and negative.

Cosine reflex $XOP_4 = OR_4$ to the right and positive.

Tangent reflex $XOP_4 = \dfrac{\sin XOP_4}{\cos XOP_4} = \dfrac{\text{negative}}{\text{positive}}$ and is negative.

In right-angled triangle P_4R_4O

Sine $P_4OR_4 = P_4R_4$

Cosine $P_4OR_4 = OR_4$

Tangent $P_4OR_4 = \dfrac{\sin P_4OR_4}{\cos P_4OR_4}$

and all are positive.

But $P_4OR_4 = (360 - XOP_4)$.

Hence   sine $XOP_4 = -\sin(360 - XOP_4)$

cosine $XOP_4 = +\cos(360 - XOP_4)$

tangent $XOP_4 = -\tan(360 - XOP_4)$.

The radius may be considered if required to revolve still farther in an anti-clockwise direction back into the first quadrant having formed an angle greater than 360° but less than 450°. The ratios then conform to the rules for the first quadrant, *i.e.*, are equal to the ratios for an angle equal to the angle so formed minus 360°.

It follows that the ratios of an angle between 450° and 540° follow the rules for the second quadrant and so on up to any number of revolutions, it being only necessary to consider that part of the angle in excess of completed revolutions.

Summary

(1) Angles in the First Quadrant, *i.e.*, between 0° and 90°. The Sine, Cosine and Tangent are ALL positive.

(2) Angles in the Second Quadrant, *i.e.*, between 90° and 180°. The Sine is positive. The Cosine and Tangent are negative.

If the angle be A, then sine $A = +\sin(180 - A)$

cosine $A = -\cos(180 - A)$

tangent $A = -\tan(180 - A)$.

(3) Angles in the Third Quadrant, *i.e.*, between 180° and 270°. The Sine and Cosine are negative. The Tangent is positive.

If the angle be A, then sine $A = -\sin(A - 180)$

cosine $A = -\cos(A - 180)$

tangent $A = +\tan(A - 180)$.

(4) Angles in the Fourth Quadrant, *i.e.*, between 270° and 360°. The Sine is negative. The Cosine is positive. The Tangent is negative.

If the angle be A, then sine $A = -\sin(360 - A)$

cosine $A = +\cos(360 - A)$

tangent $A = -\tan(360 - A)$.

Special Cases

Referring again to *Fig.* 8 and remembering that the sine of the angle is measured on the axis YY' and the cosine is measured on the axis XX' it will readily be seen that

$$\text{Sin} \quad 0° = 0, \quad \cos \quad 0° = 1, \quad \tan \quad 0° = \frac{0}{1} = 0.$$

$$\text{Sin } 90° = 1, \quad \cos 90° = 0, \quad \tan 90° = \frac{1}{0} = \infty \text{ (infinity).}$$

Sin 180° = 0, cos 180° = −1, tan 180° = 0.

Sin 270° = −1, cos 270° = 0, tan 270° = ∞ (infinity).

The Cosecant, Secant and Cotangent of an angle are simply the reciprocals of the Sine, Cosine and Tangent respectively.

$$\text{Cosecant } A = \frac{1}{\sin A} \quad \text{or} \quad \sin A = \frac{1}{\operatorname{cosec} A},$$

the cosecant always takes the same sign as the sine.

$$\text{Secant } A = \frac{1}{\cos A} \quad \text{or} \quad \cos A = \frac{1}{\sec A},$$

the secant always takes the same sign as the cosine.

$$\text{Cotangent } A = \frac{1}{\tan A} \quad \text{or} \quad \tan A = \frac{1}{\cot A},$$

the cotangent always takes the same sign as the tangent.

It is often convenient to multiply by the cosecant instead of dividing by the sine, or to multiply by the secant instead of dividing by the cosine, or to multiply by the cotangent instead of dividing by the tangent.

The following Table shows the values of the several ratios of the angles 0°, 90°, 180°, 270° and 360° with the sign of the particular ratio of the angles between.

Students should also remember that the sine and cosine of an angle can never be numerically greater than unity, that the cosecant

	0°	1st Quadrant	90°	2nd Quadrant	180°	3rd Quadrant	270°	4th Quadrant	360°
Sine	0	+	1	+	0	−	−1	−	0
Cosine	1	+	0	−	−1	−	0	+	1
Tangent	0	+	∞	−	0	+	∞	−	0
Cosecant	∞	+	1	+	∞	−	−1	−	∞
Secant	1	+	∞	−	−1	−	∞	+	1
Cotangent	∞	+	0	−	∞	+	0	−	∞

and secant of an angle can never be numerically less than unity, and that the tangent and cotangent of an angle may have any value from zero to infinity.

In dealing with the mathematical part of the theory of the deviations of magnetic compasses in ships the following trigono-metrical relationships are used. Proofs of these relationships may be found in any text-book on Elementary Trigonometry.

(1) $\operatorname{Sin}(A + B) = \sin A \cos B + \cos A \sin B.$
(2) $\operatorname{Cos}(A + B) = \cos A \cos B - \sin A \sin B.$
(3) $\operatorname{Sin}(A - B) = \sin A \cos B - \cos A \sin B.$
(4) $\operatorname{Cos}(A - B) = \cos A \cos B + \sin A \sin B.$
(5) $\operatorname{Sin} A + \sin B = 2 \sin \frac{1}{2}(A + B) \cos \frac{1}{2}(A - B).$
(6) $\operatorname{Sin} A - \sin B = 2 \cos \frac{1}{2}(A + B) \sin \frac{1}{2}(A - B).$
(7) $\operatorname{Cos} A + \cos B = 2 \cos \frac{1}{2}(A + B) \cos \frac{1}{2}(A - B).$
(8) $\operatorname{Cos} B - \cos A = 2 \sin \frac{1}{2}(A + B) \sin \frac{1}{2}(A - B)$
     (where A is the greater angle).
(9) $\operatorname{Sin} 2A = 2 \sin A \cos A.$
(10) $\operatorname{Cos} 2A = \cos^2 A - \sin^2 A.$
(11) $1 = \operatorname{Cos}^2 A + \sin^2 A$ add 10 and 11.
(12) $2 \operatorname{Cos}^2 A = 1 + \cos 2A.$
(12a) $\operatorname{Cos}^2 A = \frac{1}{2} + \frac{1}{2} \cos 2A$ subtracting 10 from 11.
(13) $1 - 2 \operatorname{Cos} A = 2 \sin^2 A.$
(13a) $\operatorname{Sin}^2 A = \frac{1}{2} - \frac{1}{2} \cos 2A$ from 11.
(14) $\operatorname{Sin}^2 A = 1 - \cos^2 A.$
(15) $\operatorname{Cos}^2 A = 1 - \sin^2 A.$

Circular Measure

The circular measure of an angle is the ratio of the arc subtended by the angle at the centre of any circle to the radius of that circle.

The length of arc of a quadrant is $\dfrac{\pi r}{2}$, and the circular measure is therefore $\dfrac{\pi r}{2/r} = \dfrac{\pi}{2}$. The circular measure of $180°$ is thus equal to π.

The unit of circular measure is the *Radian*. The radian is the circular measure of an angle at the centre of any circle subtending an arc of the circumference equal in length to the radius.

One radian $= 57°\cdot29577\ldots$

For small angles the arc subtended is almost equal to the sine of the angle. This approximation is made use of when required. Thus $\sin \delta = \delta$ is taken to mean that $\sin \delta°$ is equal to the circular measure of $\delta°$ where $\delta°$ is a very small angle.

CHAPTER IV

MAGNETISM
General

THE Molecular Theory of Magnetism is universally accepted, though it has been modified from time to time from its original form. This theory states that all magnetic substances consist of magnetic molecules each being a minute magnet. These magnetic molecules are not necessarily chemical molecules, and it is not within the scope of this book to discuss their precise nature, which is, in the light of later investigations, atomic rather than molecular. When the substance is unmagnetised these minute magnets are not arranged in any particular direction, but are orientated indiscriminately in all directions. It can in fact be proved that they prefer this arrangement rather than to be lined up in a particular direction. Once these minute magnets are aligned, however, the mutual attraction of their poles tends to hold them in position after the removal of the external force used to align them. This alignment can be destroyed by physical vibration such as hammering, or by heating. The ease with which it can be destroyed depends on whether the substance is magnetically *hard* or magnetically *soft*.

In the case of ferrous material, the substance in which we are most interested, the terms *hard iron* and *soft iron* refer specifically to this particular property.

In pure soft iron the molecules are entirely free and, unless under the influence of some external magnetic field, the iron will be non-magnetic or un-magnetised.

This is not so in the case of hard iron. The molecules are not free to move nor are they easily moved, but once lined up in a particular direction by an external force they tend to remain in that direction indefinitely, and the iron is said to be permanently magnetised. It will suffice to mention here that these so-called permanent magnets are, apart from the effects of vibration or heating, not truly permanent, but tend gradually to lose their magnetism during the course of time. Magnets made of magnetically hard substances are normally referred to as *permanent magnets*, and for the purposes of this book the effects of all iron of this nature will be covered by the term *permanent magnetism*.

What, then, of the material used in shipbuilding? The major portion is of mild steel. This material cannot be considered as either magnetically hard or magnetically soft, it has in fact both these properties as well as every intermediate type that can be considered lying between the two. Some groups of the molecules act entirely as in the case of those of soft iron, while other groups are progressively less easily disturbed, till we find that some behave exactly as the molecules of hard iron. This complicated state of affairs would at first appear to make the investigation of its effects on the compass very involved, but fortunately this is not the case. It is possible to separate the soft iron effects and the hard iron effects, and as far as the investigations are concerned, the effects appear as if there were in fact soft iron material and hard iron material in the ship as separate entities, together with material the effects of which lie somewhere between the two. These latter effects will subsequently be referred to as being due to *sub-permanent magnetism*. In some text-books this is referred to as retentive magnetism.

The term *effects* continually recurs in the text of this chapter, and it must be emphasised that though we know that the material of which the ship is built is chiefly mild steel, and that though the effects obtained indicate that there is apparently both hard and soft iron present, the effects are real and continuously there and are the cause of the deviation or deflection of the compass needle from the direction of Magnetic North. It is these effects which we measure in terms of the deviation caused and for which we compensate, using permanent magnets suitably disposed to compensate for the hard iron effects and soft iron suitably disposed to compensate for the soft iron effects.

It is the case, unfortunately, that at any given time of investigation the sub-permanent effects appear to be permanent and merely modify temporarily the permanent effect for which compensation is made. It is chiefly for this reason that a ship requires to be swung periodically to have the positions or the number of the correctors used in previous compensations suitably adjusted to allow for the change in this sub-permanent part of her magnetic field.

As the change in the sub-permanent magnetic field is normally relatively slow, so that the increase in the deviations caused by this change is not rapid, it does not involve a very frequent adjustment of the correctors. Usually if the ship is swung for adjustment at intervals of about twelve months the deviation on any direction of the ship's head will be kept sufficiently small for all practical purposes.

There are, however, circumstances under which a ship may have her magnetic field considerably altered both in direction and amount, and which may render earlier or more frequent adjustment necessary. This may be if the ship has been struck by lightning (*see note at end of chapter*), or if her cargo has been loaded or discharged by means of electro-magnets, or if the ship has suffered severe damage, as in collision, or has undergone material structural alteration. The carriage of relatively large quantities of magnetic material as cargo, such as steel rails or some types of iron ore may also cause marked changes in the deviations of the compass. When steering one course for a considerable time the ship may also acquire sub-permanent magnetism, of which the poles will be in the magnetic meridian relative to her head.

The ship's officer must therefore realise that although the ship's compasses may be regularly adjusted by a qualified compass adjuster, he must always be on the alert and be able to anticipate changes that may occur in the deviations, due to limitations in the method of adjustment or due to circumstances over which the compass adjuster has no control.

Note. In January 1949 while on station in the North Atlantic the S.S. *Weather Recorder* was struck by lightning during a severe storm. Previous to being struck the maximum deviation of the standard compass on any heading was $3\frac{1}{2}°$, after the incident the deviations were found to range from a minimum of $4°$ to a maximum of $31°$ as shown in column 1 of the analysis of the ship's deviations given on page 111a to which the reader is referred. Subsequent observations indicated that the deviations, in this particular case, took about six months to settle down so that during this time frequent adjustment of the correctors was required. The above information was obtained from, and permission to publish kindly given by, the Director of the Meteorological Office of the Air Ministry, Harrow, Middlesex.

CHAPTER V

FUNDAMENTAL FACTS OF MAGNETISM

Magnetic Poles. If a bar magnet is dipped into iron filings it will be found that the filings adhere most freely at and near the ends of the bar. These places are called the poles of the magnet.

If the magnet be suspended freely it will be found that one of the poles will always point to the Magnetic North providing no other magnetic field is present. This pole is called the *north seeking pole* or north pole of the magnet. The other pole is called the *south seeking pole* or the south pole of the magnet. The north seeking end of the magnet is often painted red and marked with a letter *N*, the south seeking end is then painted blue and marked with a letter *S*. When paint is not used and when only one end is marked, it is invariably the north end. A line drawn through the magnet in the direction of its internal field, *i.e.*, joining its poles, is called the *magnetic axis* of the magnet, and a line at right angles to this direction midway between the poles is called the *neutral axis* of the magnet.

Magnetic poles exert a force upon one another. Like poles repel, and unlike poles attract one another. The force between two poles is dependent upon their distance apart.

The strength of the north and south poles of a magnet is equal. If a bar magnet is placed upon a float in a bowl of water so that it is free to move in any direction, it will be found that the magnet will rotate with its float until the north seeking end points north and, of course, the south seeking end points south, but it will not move either toward the north or south. The attraction of the north end toward the north is therefore exactly equal to the attraction of the south end toward the south.

Magnetic Field. In general terms the magnetic field of a magnet may be defined as a region round it throughout which its influence may be detected. The term, however, is usually reckoned to have a more definite and restricted meaning. If a single magnetic pole could be placed at any point near a magnet it would experience a force in a definite direction, and if free to move it would travel in this direction. This is called the direction of the magnetic field at that point.

If a very short, freely suspended, compass needle be brought near to the end of a bar magnet, it will be found that one end of the needle will point directly toward the pole of the bar magnet, and it can be shown that the magnetic field radiates in all directions from the pole away from the length of the magnet.

If the needle be brought vertically over one pole of the bar magnet lying on a table, the needle will take up a vertical position, and if carried slowly along the length of the magnet toward the other pole it will gradually tilt out of the vertical until at mid length it will be seen to be horizontal. As the other end of the bar magnet is approached the opposite end of the compass needle will start to dip below the horizontal and continue to do so increasingly until it reaches the other pole, when it will be seen to stand vertical again with its opposite end downward. The compass needle may be said to have followed the direction of the lines of force of the magnet between its poles.

Lines of force are said to arise on a north pole of a magnet and end on a south pole. No two lines of force can meet or cross one another.

It will be seen later that this conception of lines of force may be used as a quantitative representation of the strength of the magnetic field at any particular point in it. It is a useful idea in so far as it helps one to visualise the field in a definite manner.

Magnetic Pole Strength. The pole strength of a magnet is conveniently defined as the number of unit poles acting together which are required to make up an equal pole strength.

The Inverse Square Law. It can be proved that in all cases where an effect is radially and uniformly distributed with respect to a point, the effect per unit area falls off inversely as the square of the distance from the point.

The effect on a point magnetic pole due to another point magnetic pole follows the same law. This can be proved experimentally by means of a magnetometer.

We can say therefore: "The force between two point poles varies directly as their pole strengths and inversely as the square of their distance apart."

Magnetic Intensity or Magnetic Field Strength. It has been shown that a magnetic field has a definite direction at every point in it. In order to define the force at any point in the field it is necessary to think of its effect on an imaginary unit pole placed at that point.

The strength of field or magnetic intensity at any point in a magnetic field is the force which would be exerted on a unit north pole placed at this point. This quantity is usually denoted in text-books by the letter H and is used in the general sense, but in compass work H is taken to mean the strength of the earth's horizontal force in particular. If the pole strength placed in the field of intensity H is not of unit strength, but is, say, m units, then the force exerted on it is mH newtons.

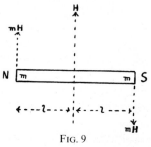

FIG. 9

Magnetic Moment of a Magnet. Consider a magnet NS (*Fig.* 9) of pole strength m placed at right angles to the earth's field of intensity H. Let $2l$ be the length between the poles of the magnet Each pole experiences a force of mH newtons, and as the forces act in opposite directions they constitute a couple. The turning moment of a couple is the product of one of the equal forces and the perpendicular distance between them. In this case the moment of the couple is $mH \times 2l$, which may be written $H \times 2ml$. The quantity

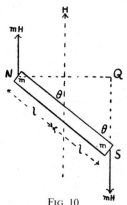

FIG. 10

$2ml$ is called the *Magnetic Moment M* of the magnet, where m is the pole strength and $2l$ the distance between the poles. The moment of the couple can then be written HM.

The length $2l$ is not generally the length of the magnet, and m and l are indefinite quantities, but the magnetic moment M is a definite quantity which can be measured with the aid of a magneto-meter. Actually further experiments could then be made in order to determine the length $2l$ or what is generally termed the *equivalent length* of the magnet. (See page 48.)

Next consider the couple acting on the magnet when inclined at any angle θ to the earth's field H (*Fig.* 10).

The force on each pole is still mH, but the perpendicular distance between the forces is now NQ.

$$\frac{NQ}{NS} = \frac{NQ}{2l} = \sin\theta \qquad \therefore\ NQ = 2l\sin\theta.$$

$$\therefore\ \text{Moment of couple} = H2ml\sin\theta = HM\sin\theta.$$

Intensity of Magnetisation. The magnetic moment of a magnet is a quantity which will vary according to the size and the material of which the magnet is made, and so we need some more definite standard in order to ascertain the intensity of the magnetisation of the material. Assuming the body to be evenly magnetised, the magnetic moment per unit volume, *i.e.*, per cubic metre, will give a definite standard for comparison and other purposes. In order to obtain this it is only necessary to divide the magnetic moment of the magnetised body by its volume in cubic metres, thus

$$\text{Intensity of Magnetisation} = \frac{\text{Magnetic Moment}}{\text{Volume of magnet}}$$

$$\text{or} \quad J = \frac{M}{V} \quad \text{or} \quad \frac{m}{A}$$

Magnetic Induction or **Magnetic Flux Density.** The magnetic induction is the flux per unit area at right angles to the direction of the field. The flux density in a medium is the sum of the flux density in a vacuum (B_0) and the flux density due to magnetisation of the medium $\left(J = \dfrac{m}{A}\right)$

$$B = B_0 + J$$

The unit of flux density is the tesla (T) or weber per square metre (Wb/m^2).

Demagnetisation. When magnetic induction is produced in magnetic material by an external force so that poles are set up in the material, they will always produce an external field which is in opposition to the inducing field.

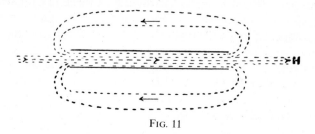

FIG. 11

Figure 11 shows a soft-iron bar under the influence of an external force H. At the middle of the magnet its field is opposed to the magnetising field H and therefore exerts a demagnetising effect on the bar.

The effect is the same in the case of a permanent magnet. The poles produce a field which opposes the magnetising field within the bar. It is for the purpose of removing this effect that permanent magnets are often provided with soft-iron keepers, the keepers producing poles equal and opposite to those of the magnet and being very nearly coincident in position with them, these poles produce a field equal and opposite to the demagnetising field.

The demagnetising effect depends on the geometrical form of the magnetised body. In the case of a very long iron wire parallel to the field, the demagnetising effect is negligible owing to the great distance between the poles. For a wire of length equal to 500 times its diameter the demagnetising effect decreases the field by about six per cent.

Magnetic Susceptibility. Some magnetic materials are more susceptible to magnetisation by induction than others. The intensity of magnetisation depends on the strength of the inducing field and upon the nature of the material. The ratio of the intensity of magnetisation produced to the strength of field producing it is called the Magnetic Susceptibility of the material, usually written k.

$$\text{Thus} \quad k = \frac{J}{H}$$

where J is the intensity of magnetisation, and H is the strength of the external inducing field.

Magnetic Permeability. The ratio of the magnetic flux density produced in a medium to the strength of the magnetic field producing it is known as the absolute permeability ( )

$$= \frac{B}{H}$$

The absolute permeability of a vacuum $= 4\pi\, 10^{-7}$.

Given the flux density the field strength can be obtained from

$$H = \frac{B}{\mu}$$

$$= \frac{B}{\mu_0} \quad \text{in a vacuum}$$

Consider an isolated pole of strength m webers at the centre of a sphere of radius r metres. The total flux outward from the sphere is m webers. The flux density (B) on the surface of the sphere is given by:

$$B = \frac{m}{4\pi r^2}$$

The field strength

$$H = \frac{m}{4\pi\mu r^2}$$

The absolute permeability of air may be assumed to be the same as for a vacuum, so if the medium is air the field strength due to an isolated pole at distance d metres is given by:

$$H = \frac{m}{4\pi\mu_0 r^2}$$

The force exerted on a pole of m units placed in a field of intensity H is mH newtons.

The force between two poles, m_1 and m_2, at a distance of d metres apart in a vacuum, or air, is therefore:

$$F = \frac{m_1 m_2}{4\pi\mu_0 d^2} \quad \text{newtons}$$

The equation is only true, however, if the intervening medium between the poles is air (theoretically it should be a vacuum). The force will vary if the medium between the poles is a magnetic material, it will still vary directly as the pole strengths and inversely as the square of the distance, but the force will be less if the medium is a magnetic material than if it is air. The force, therefore, also depends on a quality in the medium between the poles which is called its relative permeability. It is thus necessary to introduce this factor into the equation in order that it may hold good whatever the material in which the magnetic poles are placed. The relative permeability of a material is indicated by the symbol μ_r(Mu) and the equation then becomes

$$F = \frac{m_1 m_2}{4\pi\mu_0\mu_r d^2}$$

The value μ_r for air may be taken as unity.

It will be realised that magnetic susceptibility and magnetic permeability are very similar quantities, the former depending on the material in which a field is inducing magnetisation and the latter on the material or medium through which the lines of force of the inducing field have to pass.

Neither of these quantities are constant and both vary in a complex manner, but for the purposes of this book it will suffice if the student has a general understanding of the various terms relating to the properties of magnetic material.

The Strength of Field due to a Bar Magnet at two particular positions with reference to the magnet. First consider the field strength at a point P on a line passing through the poles of the magnet (*Fig.* 12). In other words the magnet is end-on to the point P.

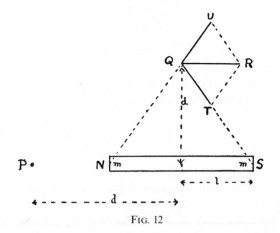

FIG. 12

Let a unit north pole be placed at P. Let the pole strength of the magnet be m and the equivalent length be $2l$. Let d be the distance of P from the centre of the magnet.

Then the force on the unit pole due to $N = \dfrac{m}{4\pi\mu_0(d - l)^2}$ and the force on the unit pole due to $S = \dfrac{m}{4\pi\mu_0(d + l)^2}$. These two forces are acting in the same line but in opposite senses, therefore the

$$
\begin{aligned}
\text{resultant force} &= \frac{m}{4\pi\mu_0(d - l)^2} - \frac{m}{4\pi\mu_0(d + l)^2} \\
&= \frac{m(d + l)^2 - m(d - l)^2}{4\pi\mu_0(d - l)^2(d + l)^2} \\
&= \frac{m(d^2 + 2dl + l^2) - m(d^2 - 2dl + l^2)}{4\pi\mu_0(d^2 - l^2)^2} \\
&= \frac{m \times 4dl}{4\pi\mu_0(d^2 - l^2)^2} \quad \text{or} \quad \frac{4ml \times d}{4\pi\mu_0(d^2 - l^2)^2}.
\end{aligned}
$$

But $2ml$ is the magnetic moment (M) of the magnet,

$$
\text{strength of field at } P = \frac{2Md}{4\pi\mu_0(d^2 - l^2)^2}
$$

If P is at a considerable distance from the magnet so that l, the half length, is very small compared with d, it can be neglected and the expression becomes $\dfrac{2Md}{4\pi\mu_0 d^4}$ and the field strength can then be written $\dfrac{2M}{4\pi\mu_0 d^3}$.

Next take a point Q on a line bisecting the magnet at right angles, in other words the magnet is broadside-on to the point Q. Imagine a unit pole to be placed at Q. The force on the unit pole due to N is $\dfrac{m}{4\pi\mu_0 NQ^2}$ and the force on the unit pole due to S is $\dfrac{m}{4\pi\mu_0 SQ^2}$ and $NQ = SQ$. If these forces are represented by QU and QT respectively (*Fig. 11*), then QR represents the resultant force, whose direction is parallel to the magnet. Complete the parallelogram.

The triangles QRU and NSQ are similar,

$$\frac{QR}{QU} = \frac{NS}{NQ} \quad \text{and} \quad QR = \frac{QU \times NS}{NQ}.$$

But $QU = \dfrac{m}{4\pi\mu_0 NQ^2}$ and $NS = 2l$

$$QR = \frac{2ml}{4\pi\mu_0 NQ^3} = \frac{M}{4\pi\mu_0 NQ^3}.$$

Also from *Fig.* 11, $NQ^2 = d^2 + l^2$

$$\therefore \quad NQ^3 = (d^2 + l^2)^{3/2}.$$

Hence field strength at $Q = \dfrac{M}{4\pi\mu_0(d^2 + l^2)^{3/2}}.$

As before, if l can be considered very small compared with d, it can be neglected and the expression becomes

$$\text{field strength at } Q = \frac{M}{4\pi\mu_0 d^3}.$$

From the foregoing it will be seen that the effect of a magnet when placed end-on is twice the effect when placed broadside-on.

It will also be noted that in the end-on position of P the distance d and the half length l from the centre of the magnet are in one and the same direction, while in the broadside-on position the distance d from the centre is in a direction at right angles to the length of the magnet.

Now consider the unit Pole P to be rotated at radius d from the centre O of the magnet clockwise to an angle θ with the length-wise direction of the magnet (*Fig.* 12a).

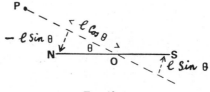

The effective half length l of the magnet in the direction OP becomes $l \cos \theta$ and in the direction anti-clockwise and at right angles to OP, $-l \sin \theta$ and $l \sin \theta$ in the clockwise direction. Using the same arguments as in the case of the end-on position and assuming that l is small compared with d it can be seen that the field strength at P in the direction $OP = \dfrac{2M \cos \theta}{4\pi\mu_0 d^3}$ and the field strength at P in the direction $90°$ anti-clockwise from OP is $\dfrac{-M \sin \theta}{4\pi\mu_0 d^3}$ and conversely $\dfrac{M \sin \theta}{4\pi\mu_0 d^3}$ in the direction $90°$ clockwise from OP.

If we make θ equal to zero, i.e. the original end-on position of P then $\cos \theta = 1$ and the expression becomes $\dfrac{2M}{4\pi\mu_0 d^3}$ as before, also if $\theta = 90°$, i.e. the broadside-on position then $\sin \theta = 1$ and the expression becomes $\dfrac{M}{4\pi\mu_0 d^3}$ as before.

The equations relating to the various properties are summarised below. It will assist the student considerably if he correlates these equations by substitution of terms from one equation into another by normal algebraic process.

Intensity of Magnetisation $\quad J = \dfrac{M}{V}$

Magnetic Induction $\quad B = H + 4\pi J$

Magnetic Susceptibility $\quad k = \dfrac{J}{B_0} = \dfrac{J}{\mu_0 H}$

Magnetic Permeability $\quad \mu = \dfrac{B}{H}$

Force between two poles $\quad F = \dfrac{m_1 m_2}{4\pi\mu d^2} \quad$ or $\quad \dfrac{m_1 m_2}{4\pi\mu_0 d^2} \quad$ in air

Field Strength $\quad H = \dfrac{m}{4\pi\mu d^2} \quad$ or $\quad \dfrac{m}{4\pi\mu_0 d^2} \quad$ in air

Magnetic Field due to an Electric Current. It can be shown that when a current of electricity is passed through a long straight wire a magnetic field is set up round the wire which is circular in shape, the lines of force being concentric with the wire, and the plane of the field everywhere perpendicular to the wire.

Figure 13 represents a wire passed through a sheet of paper, with a current flowing through the wire vertically upward perpendicular to the plane of the paper. The concentric circles represent the lines of force running in the direction of the arrows.

The following rule by Ampère is useful in ascertaining the direction toward which the north end of a compass needle would be deflected if the direction of the current flowing in the wire is known, or conversely to ascertain the direction in which the current is flowing if the direction of the deflection of the compass needle is known.

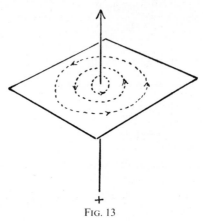

FIG. 13

Ampère's Rule. Suppose a man to be swimming in the wire in the direction of the current, and that he turns so as to face the compass needle, then the north-seeking pole of the needle will be deflected towards the swimmer's left hand.

For the benefit of students who, due to a study of Radar or other reasons, have a knowledge of the Electron Theory, it must be emphasised that the direction of the current referred to here is in the normal conventional sense, *i.e.* from positive to negative, or against the flow of electrons.

Figure 14 shows the effect if the wire is made to conform to a circular shape, the current flowing through it in the direction of the arrows. The plane of the circle is supposed to be perpendicular to the horizontal plane of the paper and so placed that the latter bisects the circle so that half the circle of wire is above the surface of the paper and half below it, only the lower portion of the latter being visible.

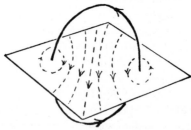

FIG. 14

The lines of force near to the wire approximate to circles, while at the centre of the paper the lines are straight. The arrows on the lines of force will be seen to conform to Ampère's rule.

Magnetic Field of a Solenoid. A solenoid is a uniform helix with its neighbouring turns spaced just enough to avoid short-circuiting, though, of course, the wire may be insulated. Investigation will show that the magnetic field is similar to that of a permanent bar magnet. *Figure* 15 represents a section of such a solenoid. As

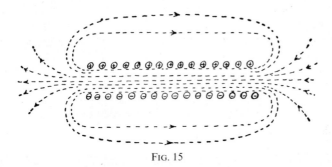

FIG. 15

indicated by the signs, the current is flowing away from the reader in the bottom of the wire and toward him in the top sections. The direction of the lines of force is as might be expected, having regard to Ampère's rule.

The following two rules connecting direction of field and direction of current are also very convenient:

(i) If, looking endways at a solenoid the direction of the current is clockwise, that end is the south pole. This rule may be remembered by thinking of a letter "S" inscribed in a circle, the ends of the letter forming arrows on the circumference indicating the direction of the current in the solenoid (*Fig.* 16).

FIG. 16

(ii) Place the right hand over the turns of the coil with the finger-tips pointing in the direction in which the current is flowing, the outstretched thumb will then point to the north pole of the solenoid.

The unit of electric current is the ampere (A). It is that current which flowing in each of two infinitely long parallel straight wires of negligible cross-sectional area, separated by a distance of one metre in vacuo, produces between them a force of 2×10^{-7} newtons per metre of their length.

The unit of magnetic field strength is the ampere per metre (A/m). One ampere per metre is the strength of magnetic field inside a long solenoid wound with n turns of wire per metre of its length, carrying a current I, such that the product nI is one ampere turn per metre.

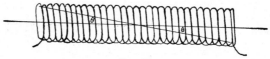

FIG. 17

The strength of field inside a long solenoid (*Fig.* 17) is given by:

$$H = nI \text{ amperes per metre.}$$

If a solenoid is fitted with a soft-iron core the medium is then no longer air, and will have a relative permeability whose value is greater than unity. The equation then becomes

$$H = \mu_r I n$$

It will thus be realised that a solenoid with a core of high permeability (the relative permeability of soft iron may be of the order of 2,000), becomes a powerful magnet when the current is flowing.

If two parallel solenoids are wound on the same circuit but in opposite directions and fitted with soft-iron cores, that is to say if the wire on one core is wound clockwise and then continued round the other core in an anti-clockwise direction (*Fig.* 18) we have what is termed an *Electro-magnet*.

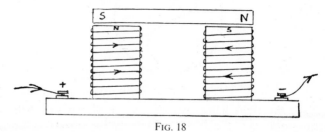

FIG. 18

By placing a bar of magnetic material across the two adjacent poles the bar will become magnetised when the current flows. If the bar is of a magnetically hard character it will become a permanent magnet with polarity as shown in the figure. This is the usual method by which permanent magnets are made. It is also the principle upon which is based the construction of the large electro-magnets used in the loading and discharging of cargoes of scrap iron, etc., at many ports where the trade in such materials is considerable.

CHAPTER VI

THE EARTH'S MAGNETISM

THAT the earth has a magnetic field is obvious from the fact that a freely suspended magnet will come to rest in a direction approximately North and South. In other words, the magnet will settle in a direction of the earth's field at the place at which the magnet is being used.

At most places on the earth's surface this direction will not be horizontal nor will it lie in the geographical meridian. In the British Isles the north-seeking end of a freely suspended magnet will dip below the horizontal and be inclined at an angle to the westward of True North.

In general, if the magnet were carried northward over the earth's surface following the surface direction of its north-seeking end, we should find that the magnet would dip at an ever-increasing angle from the horizontal until, eventually, we should arrive at an area where the magnet would take up a vertical position and have no directional value whatever. On the other hand, if we proceeded southward following the south-seeking end, we should find that the angle from the horizontal would gradually decrease until, when somewhere in the vicinity of the geographical equator, the magnet would lie in an exactly horizontal position. Continuing southward the south-seeking end would dip below the horizontal until eventually we should reach another area where the magnet would assume a vertical position, this time with the south-seeking end downward.

This imaginary experiment would, therefore, give similar results to the experiment described on page 23, when the effect of passing a small compass needle over the length of a bar magnet was noted.

In fact the area on the earth's surface where a freely suspended magnet would set vertically with its north-seeking end downward is called the *North Magnetic Pole*, and that area where such a magnet would set vertically with its south-seeking end downward is called the *South Magnetic Pole*.

It should be noted that the north magnetic pole of the earth is of the same affinity as the south pole of the magnet, and would conventionally be coloured blue. The south magnetic pole of the earth is of the same affinity as the north pole of the magnet and would conventionally be coloured red.

It would thus appear that the earth's magnetic field is similar to that of a bar magnet. As a first approximation this is substantially correct. The general magnetic field of the earth is similar to that which could be expected at the surface if a short but strongly magnetised bar magnet were located at the centre. This partly explains the fact that the magnetic poles are relatively large areas, due to the spreading out of the lines of force from the magnet, it also gives a reason for the direction of the field being horizontal in the vicinity of the equator. It is most improbable, however, that there is such a magnet at the centre of the earth, and in actual fact the cause of the field is still being investigated by many learned scientists. No theory put forward up to the present has found general acceptance.

As far as we are concerned, the *idea* of the magnet at the centre of the earth is useful as it helps us to visualise the general form of the magnetic field as it is known to be despite the many imperfections which will become apparent as we proceed.

The area termed the North Magnetic Pole is situated in approximately 71° N., 96° W. and the South Magnetic Pole in 73° S., 156° E. These positions are very approximate, but one fact emerges, namely, that the south pole is not diametrically opposite to the north pole.

A line joining all positions on the earth's surface where the direction of the magnetic field is horizontal is called the *Magnetic Equator* or Line of No Dip. It is not a perfect circle but a wavy line which crosses the geographical equator in two points, from north to south in about 35° W. and from south to north in about 170° W., reaching its most northerly position in central Africa and most southerly position in Brazil.

Theoretically the maximum strength of field should be at the poles, actually the field strength in certain other areas in both high north and south latitudes is found to exceed that at the magnetic poles. These areas are called *Magnetic Foci*.

In order to determine the direction and force of the earth's magnetism at any place we require to know three of four *magnetic elements*. The four elements are Variation, Dip, Horizontal Force and Vertical Force.

Magnetic Variation or Declination at a place on the earth's surface is the horizontal angle contained between the true meridian and the direction of the lines of force of the earth's magnetic field at the place. It should be noted that this latter direction is not necessarily in the exact direction of the magnetic pole from the place; this is due to slight distortions in the earth's field of a semi-local character. This fact is verified if one examines a Variation chart.

Lines joining places on a chart having the same value of Variation are called *Isogonal Lines.* Lines drawn through places where the Variation is zero are called *Agonic Lines.*

When the direction of the earth's field inclines to the left of True North, that is when a compass needle, under the influence of the field at the place, points to the West of True North, the Variation is said to be Westerly. When the inclination is to the right of True North the Variation is said to be Easterly.

Variation at all places on the earth is undergoing a long period change. One theory suggests that the magnetic poles revolve round the geographical poles once in about 960 years, but the rate of change from earlier observations does not appear to be constant. Variation also goes through annual and daily alterations in its value, these are small, however, and do not affect the navigator. Variation charts, showing Isogonal lines covering the world and indicating the mean annual change, are published by the British Admiralty at intervals of about five years.

In order to measure the variation it is necessary to ensure that no local magnetic field is present. If conducting such a measurement at sea, it would be essential that the whole ship were built of non-magnetic material. A special magnetic needle is required and, for accurate observations to minutes of arc, an instrument such as the Kew Magnetometer is used. The bearing of a suitable object is obtained with the instrument, the needle of which is then turned over and the observation repeated. The mean of the bearings is then compared with the known or calculated true bearing of the object, and the Variation found. The reason for turning the needle over is that its magnetic axis may not be parallel with the geometric axis. If the line joining the poles of the needle is not parallel with the geometric or visual axis, the needle will point to one side of the magnetic meridian at the place, but when turned over will point exactly at the same amount on the other side of the magnetic meridian. The mean of the two directions will therefore be the correct direction of the magnetic meridian at the place. For ordinary purposes of navigation, if the standard compass is well placed magnetically, the variation may be ascertained by swinging the ship slowly in azimuth and observing the compass bearing of a celestial body, suitably placed, on eight or more equidistant points. The mean of the differences between the compass bearings and the corresponding true bearings will be the approximate variation.

Magnetic Dip or Inclination. The vertical angle contained between the horizontal and the direction of the earth's magnetic field at any given place is called the Angle of Dip. Dip is conventionally considered positive when the north end of a freely suspended magnetised needle dips below the horizontal, and negative when the south end dips below the horizontal. Hence all angles of dip north of the magnetic equator will be positive and all angles of dip south of the magnetic equator will be negative.

Lines drawn on a chart joining all places for which dip has the same value are called *Isoclinals*. The line joining all places where no dip occurs is called the *Aclinic Line*; it is also referred to as the Magnetic Equator, and has already been described.

The value of the angle of dip at all places undergoes similar changes to those described for variation. The cause of the changes is not yet entirely understood. Charts of the world, showing lines of equal dip and indicating the mean annual change, are published by the British Admiralty in the same way as Variation charts.

Dip is usually measured by means of an instrument called a Dip Circle. This consists of a vertical circle and scale at the centre of which the dip needle is suspended on a fine steel axle resting on two agate knife edges. The stand contains a horizontal azimuth circle to facilitate placing the magnet in the plane of the magnetic meridian. A spirit level and levelling screws are fitted to the stand. Low-powered microscopes with cross wires and verniers are fitted to the framework for greater accuracy of measurement.

Once the instrument has been levelled and its plane placed in the magnetic meridian there are four potential sources of error to be allowed for, involving the making of sixteen observations:

(1) The axis of rotation of the magnet may not be at the centre of the scale. Both ends of the pointer are therefore read and the mean of the readings taken.

(2) The zero line of the circle may not be horizontal. By rotating the dip circle through 180° this error is reversed, but the mean of the upper and lower readings must again be taken and a mean of the means made.

(3) The magnetic axis of the magnet may not coincide with its geometric axis. The magnet must therefore be reversed on its bearings and the four readings obtained by (1) and (2) repeated.

(4) The centre of gravity of the needle may not lie in the axis of rotation. The magnet must therefore be remagnetised so that its polarity is reversed and all eight readings described in (1), (2) and (3) repeated.

Generally, all sixteen readings are tabulated and their mean is taken as the true dip.

A more modern method of measuring dip is by means of an electrical instrument called a *Dip Inductor*. In this instrument a coil is rotated about an axis whose direction can be varied and/or measured. It is moved until a galvanometer in the circuit registers no induced current in the rotating coil. The axis of rotation is then aligned along the field so that its angle of inclination is the Dip.

The Earth's Total Force or Magnetic Intensity. The value of the earth's total force at a given place is seldom required to be known, and is also difficult to measure. It is usual to measure the horizontal component of the total force, normally referred to as the earth's *Horizontal Force*. Then, if the Dip is known, the total force can be calculated, this also applies to the vertical component or earth's *Vertical Force*. (See page 8.)

A knowledge of the values of the Horizontal and Vertical Forces respectively is of great practical value. *Figure* 19 shows the relationship between Dip, Horizontal Force, Vertical Force and Total Force.

If the vector AB represents the Total Force T and θ is the angle of Dip, then AC represents the Horizontal Force H and CB represents the Vertical Force Z.

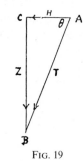

Given θ and H, then $\dfrac{Z}{H} = \tan\theta$, and $Z = H\tan\theta$

also $\dfrac{H}{T} = \cos\theta$, and $T = H\sec\theta$

and $T^2 = H^2 + Z^2$.

FIG. 19

As stated, it is usual to measure the horizontal component of the earth's total magnetic force or field strength at a given place. This is done by means of a magnetometer and a vibration experiment. The two experiments are required in order to obtain two equations as two unknown quantities are involved; one is H, the force we require, and the other is the magnetic moment of the magnet used in the experiments. The magnetic moment can be found if required or simply eliminated by the simple algebraic process of combining the simultaneous equations formed from the results of the two experiments. The full procedure is described in the next chapter.

Both H and Z may now be measured by more modern electrical instruments called coil galvanometers. These instruments can be specially designed to measure H or to measure Z, but are not entirely satisfactory, as they are difficult to calibrate accurately, though it is probably only a matter of time before they entirely replace the magnetometer for this purpose.

The strength of the earth's magnetic field is subject to periodic changes covering long and short periods of time, but little is known of the cause or precise value of the long-period change. It is known that when sunspot activity is pronounced short-period fluctuations are more marked, and that on some days, called *magnetically quiet days*, the elements undergo smooth regular variations, while on others, called *magnetically active days*, they are more or less disturbed. There appear also to be fluctuations due to daylight hours and due to dark hours as well as to a lunar cycle. These minor fluctuations in the values of the elements are small and do not affect the navigator. As in the case of Variation and Dip, charts of the world are published showing the values of H and Z for all places on the earth's surface together with the mean annual change.

These values are now given in micro-teslas, units of magnetic flux density. A micro-tesla is one millionth part of a tesla. To convert flux density in micro-teslas to magnetic field strength in ampere metres the following conversion factor should be used:

$$H = \frac{B}{\mu_0}$$

$$1 \text{ tesla} = \frac{1}{\mu_0} \text{ A/m}$$

$$= \frac{10^7}{4\pi} \text{ A/m}$$

$$1 \text{ micro-tesla} = \frac{10^7}{4\pi} \times 10^{-6} \text{ A/m}$$

$$= \frac{10}{4\pi} \text{ A/m}$$

$$= 0{\cdot}8 \text{ A/m approximately}$$

i.e., values of H and Z given in micro-teslas may be converted to magnetic field strength in ampere metres by multiplying by the factor $\dfrac{10}{4\pi}$, which is approximately 0·8.

For the purpose of compass calculations it is not usually necessary to make the conversion. The values of H and Z in micro-teslas may be assumed to be values of field strength in ampere metres without affecting the answers obtained.

Magnetic Storms. These are usually assumed to be connected with large sunspot activity. The overall intensity of the disturbance increases from low to high latitudes reaching a maximum in about 67°, the Auroral Zone, and then decreases somewhat toward the magnetic poles. Very little change is observed in the Variation in low and middle latitudes during the period of the storm, a fortunate circumstance from the navigator's point of view. The chief variation occurs in the value of H. The horizontal force at first increases rapidly and remains above its normal value for a period of from two to four hours. Having quickly attained a maximum, H decreases and after several hours attains a minimum which is much more below the normal value than the maximum was above it. From this minimum there is a slow recovery toward normal value which is not usually reached for several days. The value of Z undergoes similar changes but much smaller than those of H and in the opposite way, when H increases Z decreases and *vice versa*. A noteworthy feature of the more outstanding storms is that they commence suddenly and at almost the same instant all over the earth.

Local Magnetic Disturbance. In the course of numerous magnetic surveys, which have been carried out all over the world, it has been found that there are certain localities wherein the local values of the magnetic elements differ considerably from the values anticipated by the general results of the survey. This effect may be caused by large concentrations of magnetised ores near the surface of the earth and can be detected at sea-level in certain parts of the oceans as well as on the land.

A knowledge of the positions of these areas on the coasts and in the seas is of vital importance to the navigator. Their positions are published in the *Sailing Directions* and in other publications used in navigation, and warnings are often printed on the charts concerned.

The most marked effect of these local disturbances is the abnormal Variation which they cause. In some localities the direction of the earth's magnetic field is found to be deflected to almost 90° from its normal direction so that, for instance, a large Easterly Variation may change rapidly to a large Westerly Variation as the spot is approached. The general tendency of these disturbed areas is to attract the north-seeking end of the compass needle in North Magnetic Latitudes and to repel the north-seeking end of the needle in South Magnetic Latitudes. It is for this reason that these areas of local magnetic disturbance are often somewhat loosely referred to as areas of local magnetic attraction.

The value of the Dip and of the intensity of the magnetic field is also considerably affected in these localities, the former may be as much as 30° greater than in the immediate vicinity clear of the local field, while the horizontal field may be so reduced as to be ineffective at the compass position.

c

CHAPTER VII

MAGNETIC MEASUREMENTS

"End-on" Position of a Magnet. Let a short magnetised needle be pivoted horizontally and be lying with its axis north and south in the magnetic meridian. Now place a bar magnet with its axis in the same horizontal plane and at right angles to that of the needle and so that its length lies in the vertical plane through the pivot P of the needle (*Fig.* 20). Let the north end be the nearer pole of the magnet.

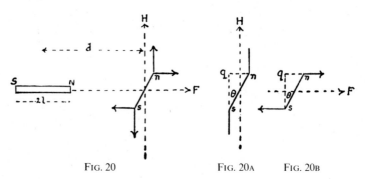

FIG. 20   FIG. 20A   FIG. 20B

The north end of the needle will be deflected away from the magnet and will come to rest at an angle (θ say) to the direction of the earth's magnetic field. Let the strength of the earth's field be H and that of the magnet be F. (The needle is assumed to be sufficiently small and the distance from the magnet sufficiently great to ensure F will have the same values at both poles north and south of the magnet.) Let m_1, M_1 and $2l_1$ be the pole strength, magnetic moment and length of the pivoted needle respectively.

It will be seen that acting on the needle there is a restoring couple due to H (*Fig.* 20A), and a disturbing couple due to F (*Fig.* 20B). As the needle is at rest these couples must be equal.

The force exerted on the poles of the needle by H is Hm_1, and the force exerted on the poles of the needle by F is Fm_1. The restoring couple due to H has already been discussed (p. 25), and was seen to be $HM \sin \theta$.

Similarly, the disturbing couple due to F

$$= Fm_1 \times nq \quad (Fig.\ 20\textsc{b})$$
$$= Fm_1 \times 2l\cos\theta$$
$$= FM_1\cos\theta$$
$$FM_1\cos\theta = HM_1\sin\theta$$
$$\text{and} \quad \frac{F}{H} = \tan\theta$$
$$F = H\tan\theta.$$

By substituting the expression for F as found on p. 29 for the end-on position we get

$$\frac{2Md}{4\pi\mu_0(d^2 - l^2)^2} = H\tan\theta,$$

where M is the magnetic moment of the magnet, d is the distance of the centre of the magnet from the needle, and l is the half-length of the magnet.

Then $\dfrac{M}{H} = \dfrac{4\pi\mu_0(d^2 - l^2)^2}{2d}\ \tan\theta$, or if l is small compared with d,

$$\frac{M}{H} = 2\pi\mu_0 d^3\tan\theta.$$

Note. If in the equation $F = H\tan\theta$, the angle of deflection is made $90°$, then $\tan\theta = \infty$ (see p. 17) and the value of F is infinitely great. This is reasonable, for as long as H has a value, the angle of deflection must be less than $90°$, however great the value of F may be. Again, if H is zero, then there can be no deflecting force as such, because F then becomes the strength of the natural field in the direction of which the needle will lie, and under the conventional terms of reference "F" would normally be called "H".

Magnet at Right Angles to the Deflected Needle. If the magnet be so adjusted that its length lies at right angles to the deflected needle (*Fig.* 21), the restoring couple is still $HM\sin\theta$ when the needle is in equilibrium. The deflecting couple exerted by the magnet is, however, FM, and is independent of the angle of deflection of the needle.

For equilibrium $FM = HM\sin\theta$

$$\text{and} \quad F = H\sin\theta.$$

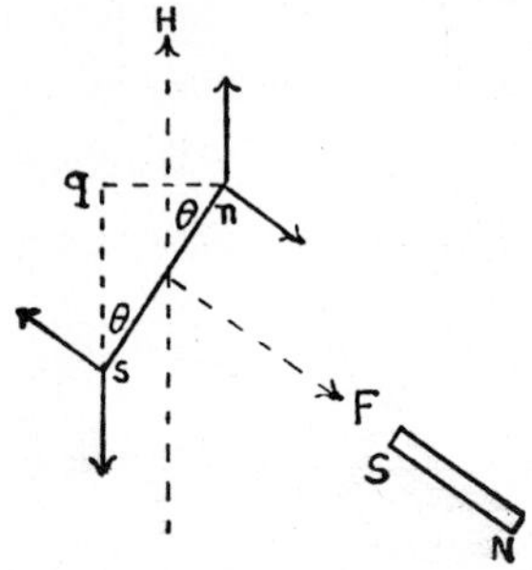

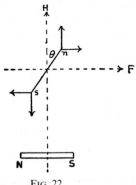

Fig. 21

If F is considered to increase while H remains constant, then $\sin \theta$ must increase in proportion if equilibrium is to be maintained. The maximum value of $\sin \theta$ is unity, and the angle of deflection will be 90°.

Hence, if the deflection is 90°, $F = H$.

The magnet will then lie in the same directional plane as H, but opposite in sense to the direction of H. In other words, F and H will be equal and opposite forces acting on the needle.

This principle is used in the Deflector Method of compass adjustment, and will be referred to again in a later chapter.

The consideration of angles of deflection greater than 90° is rather more complicated and is unnecessary for the purposes of this book.

"Broadside-on" Position of a Magnet. Let the magnet be placed so that its axis is still in the same horizontal plane and at right angles to the undisturbed needle, but so that the direction of the undisturbed needle lies in a vertical plane through the centre of the magnet perpendicular to its axis (*Fig. 22*).

Fig. 22

The needle will be deflected and come to rest at an angle (θ say) to the direction of the earth's field. As the needle is in equilibrium, the restoring couple and the disturbing couple are equal.

The restoring couple $= HM_1 \sin \theta$
The disturbing couple $= FM_1 \cos \theta$
and $F = H \tan \theta$.

Substituting the expression for F (p. 30) for the broadside-on position we get

$$\frac{M}{4\pi\mu_0(d^2 + l^2)^{3/2}} = H \tan \theta$$

$$\frac{M}{H} = 4\pi\mu_0(d^2 + l^2)^{3/2} \tan \theta$$

or if l is small compared with d,

then
$$\frac{M}{H} = 4\pi\mu_0 d^3 \tan \theta.$$

The Magnetometer. This instrument may be used for comparing the strength of magnetic fields, for comparing magnetic moments and for finding the ratio of a magnetic moment to a magnetic field strength, as is done as part of the process when determining the value of H, the horizontal component of the earth's magnetic field.

The magnetometer has a variety of forms to suit different uses, but its fundamental construction is the same in all cases. In its most simple form it consists of a short compass needle suspended on a pivot or by a fibre at the centre of a graduated circle and fitted with a long pointer. The box with a glass top containing the needle and scale is mounted on a wooden base carrying a groove and centimetre scale. A diagrammatic form of the instrument is shown in *Fig. 23.*

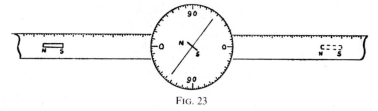

FIG. 23

The circular scale has two diametrically opposite zeros and is graduated to 90° in each direction from the zeros. The centimetre scale is graduated to record the distance from the centre of the needle along the groove.

To Make an Experiment. First the compass box must be gently rotated on the base until the line joining the two zeros of the circular scale is parallel to the centimetre scale. The base is then rotated until each end of the pointer is opposite one of the zeros on the scale. The whole system is then levelled. A bar magnet is then inserted in the groove with its middle point a specified distance, say d metres, from the pivot of the needle as measured on the centimetre scale. Its axis will be east and west.

(1) The deflection is then read from both ends of the pointer in order to correct for lack of symmetry between the scale and the pointer.

(2) The magnet is next moved laterally in the groove to the opposite side of the needle at exactly the same distance as before (see dotted position in *Fig.* 23), and the two readings for the deflection are obtained again. This is to allow for the fact that the zero of the linear scale may not be exactly at the centre of the needle.

(3) The magnet is now turned end for end and all the observations are repeated. This is done to allow for the fact that the polarity of the magnet may not be symmetrical.

We thus have eight readings, the mean of which is the deflection caused by the bar magnet at distance d metres from the centre of the needle.

Equivalent Length of a Magnet. As stated earlier it is not correct to use the length l employed in the relevant equations as half the length of the magnet. On the other hand, there must be some value of l for every magnet, such that $2ml$ is the magnetic moment of the magnet. This value is termed the *Equivalent Length.*

If the experiment described above is repeated with the same magnet at a different distance from the magnetometer needle, then if d_1 and d_2 are the two distances involved we can write

$$\frac{M}{H} = \frac{4\pi\mu_0(d_1{}^2 - l_1{}^2)^2}{2d_1} \tan\theta_1 \text{ for the first experiment,}$$

and $$\frac{M}{H} = \frac{4\pi\mu_0(d_2{}^2 - l_2{}^2)^2}{2d_2} \tan\theta_2 \text{ for the second experiment,}$$

M and H are constant and $l_1 = l_2$

$$\frac{4\pi\mu_0(d_1{}^2 - l^2)^2}{2d_1} \tan\theta_1 = \frac{4\pi\mu_0(d_2{}^2 - l^2)^2}{2d_2} \tan\theta_2$$

and since d_1, d_2, $\tan \theta_1$ and $\tan \theta_2$ are known quantities, l can be calculated.

Comparison of Magnetic Field Strengths. By performing the magnetometer experiment in two different places, using the same magnet in both cases, the field strength at the two places may be compared.

If H_1 be the field strength at the first place and H_2 be the field strength at the second place, then we can write

$$\frac{M}{H_1} = \frac{4\pi\mu_0 d_1{}^3}{2} \tan \theta_1 \qquad (1)$$

and

$$\frac{M}{H_2} = \frac{4\pi\mu_0 d_2{}^3}{2} \tan \theta_2 \qquad (2)$$

divide 2 by 1 and we get

$$\frac{H_1}{H_2} = \frac{d_2{}^3 \tan \theta_2}{d_1{}^3 \tan \theta_1}.$$

Comparison of Magnetic Moments. If two different magnets are used, H remaining constant, the ratio of their magnetic moments may be found, for using the same symbols as before we get

$$\frac{M_1}{M_2} = \frac{d_1{}^3 \tan \theta_1}{d_2{}^3 \tan \theta_2}.$$

For more accurate results the longer expression should be used.

It will be seen from the above experiments that by means of the magnetometer we can obtain from one experiment the ratio of the magnetic moment M to the field strength H, or from two experiments we can obtain the ratio of one field strength to another, or the ratio of one magnetic moment to another. In no case do we arrive at the absolute value of either H or M.

Period of Vibration of a Suspended Magnet. If the same magnet used in the magnetometer experiment is suspended in a stirrup and hung by a silk fibre and is then placed in the position of the magnetometer (removed) and protected from draughts, it will come to rest in the direction of the earth's field. It can then be made to oscillate in a horizontal plane about its axis of suspension by bringing another magnet near to the suspended magnet and withdrawing it quickly. The amplitude of the vibrations should be small and the time of a number of complete oscillations should be taken. From this result the time of one complete oscillation can be found, this is the period of the magnet. The time of one complete oscillation is time taken from passing any given position until the next passing in the *same* direction.

For such a rotation

$$\text{Angular acceleration} = \frac{\text{Applied Couple}}{\text{Moment of Inertia of the rotating system,}}$$

$$\text{and in the case} = \frac{HM \sin \theta}{I}$$

where H is the earth's horizontal field, M is the magnetic moment of the vibrating magnet, θ is the angle through which it is turned, and I is the moment of inertia of the vibrating magnet about an axis through its centre of gravity perpendicular to its length. If θ is small $\dfrac{\text{angular acceleration}}{\text{angular displacement}} = \dfrac{HM}{I}$ and is constant. The motion is therefore simple harmonic, and if T is its period, then

$$\frac{HM}{I} = \frac{4\pi^2}{T^2}$$

from which we get the normal expression

$$T = 2\pi \sqrt{\frac{I}{HM}},$$

then
$$HM = \frac{4\pi^2 I}{T^2}.$$

As I can be found, all the quantities on the right-hand side of the equation are known.

The Moment of Inertia of a body about any axis may be defined as the sum of the products of all the elementary masses which make up the whole body, and the squares of the perpendicular distances of the elementary masses from the given axis.

The moment of inertia of a solid cylindrical bar about an axis through its centre of gravity perpendicular to its length is given by

$$I = m \left(\frac{l^2}{12} + \frac{r^2}{4} \right)$$

where m is the mass of the bar, l is the length and r is the radius.

The moment of inertia of a thin rectangular bar of length l and breadth b, about an axis through its centre of gravity perpendicular to the length is given by

$$I = m \left(\frac{l^2 + b^2}{12} \right).$$

From the magnetometer experiment we have

$$\frac{M}{H} = \frac{4\pi\mu_0(d^2 - l^2)^2}{2d} \tag{1}$$

From the vibration experiment we have

$$HM = \frac{4\pi^2 I}{T^2} \tag{2}$$

Divide 2 by 1 then

$$H^2 = \frac{4\pi^2 I}{T^2} \times \frac{2d}{4\pi\mu_0(d^2 - l^2)^2}$$

whence H can be calculated.

By multiplying 2 by 1 we get

$$M^2 = \frac{2\pi^2 I}{T^2} \times \frac{4\pi\mu_0(d^2 - l^2)^2}{d}$$

or more approximately

$$M^2 = \frac{8\pi^3 \mu_0 I d^3}{T^2}$$

whence M can be calculated.

The magnetometer used for finding the value of H, the earth's horizontal force, is a much more elaborate instrument than the simple one described above. The needle is suspended by a long quartz fibre, a telescope with cross wires is fitted, and the deflection is read off on a reflected scale by the means of mirrors, thereby increasing the radius of the scale and considerably magnifying the arc. The principle and the method are, however, exactly the same as that described above.

CHAPTER VIII

THE SHIP'S MAGNETISM (Preliminary)

THE magnetic field of a ship has been discussed in a general way in Chapter III. The magnetic material of which the ship is built is chiefly mild steel, and as such is neither magnetically hard nor magnetically soft, but a complicated mixture of the two. With the exception of the part which is purely magnetically soft, the whole ship's structure becomes magnetised to a greater or lesser degree in the course of building and manufacture due to vibration and hammering in the presence of the earth's field, and more locally due to induction from electro-magnetic fields when welding equipment and other electrical devices are used as construction proceeds.

If effects due to welding, etc., are ignored and the material is considered unmagnetised until it arrives on the building site, the ship can then be considered to become a permanent magnet in the course of construction with poles lying in the direction of the earth's field.

Figures 24 and 24A indicate diagrammatically this condition: in the case of (i) a ship built in a North magnetic direction; and (ii) an East magnetic direction at a yard in the British Isles (Dip 68°), conventional colouring being used.

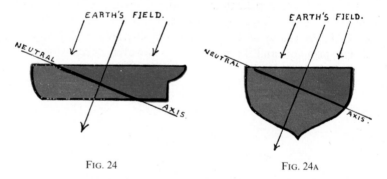

FIG. 24   FIG. 24A

These diagrams show the general tendency only, and may be quite misleading if local effects are appreciable.

The effect of the magnetisation of the ship is to cause a deflection of the north end of the compass needle away from the direction of

Magnetic North, or more accurately, away from the direction of the earth's field at the place, when the compass is placed on board the ship.

A line drawn in the direction of the earth's magnetic field at a given place is usually termed the magnetic meridian at the place, and is analogous to the term geographical meridian.

The angle through which the compass needle on board ship is deflected from the magnetic meridian due to the ship's magnetic field is called the *Deviation of the Compass*. If the north end is deflected to the eastward or clockwise, the deviation is said to be Easterly, and if deflected to the left or anticlockwise, the deviation is said to be Westerly. Easterly deviation is also considered positive and Westerly deviation negative.

Mariner's Compass. The term compass needle is meant to cover the various systems of magnetic needles found in compasses used on board ships.

This type of compass, referred to as the Mariner's Compass, is used to find the direction of the ship's head relative to the magnetic meridian and to ascertain the bearings of terrestrial and celestial objects from the ship. The compass needle is suspended so as to have freedom of movement in the horizontal plane only, it is therefore affected by the horizontal component of the earth's field alone.

In order to prevent the roll of the ship from setting up oscillations of the compass card, the disposition of the mass of the card in the various directions from the pivot is taken into account in its manufacture.

It has also been determined mathematically that the proper system of needles is that in which the mean of the angles subtended at the centre of the compass by symmetrical pairs of like poles is 60°. This arrangement also happens to be the correct arrangement magnetically, as it gives the equivalent of a short magnet placed at the centre and helps considerably to ensure that a satisfactory correction can be made.

The bowl containing the card is placed in the compass binnacle, which is designed to allow the bowl free movement in a gimbal system, so arranged that the compass remains horizontal for all movements of the ship without appreciably displacing the lubber line from the fore and aft line of the ship.

Binnacles are constructed of non-magnetic material, usually wood, and are of such a shape, size and height that bearings of terrestrial or celestial objects may be taken most conveniently. They are fitted to receive the various correctors used to counteract the ship's disturbing magnetic fields.

The correctors consist of a Flinders Bar, a bar of soft iron placed vertically on the outside of the binnacle; spheres, soft-iron solid or hollow globes, are also fitted on the outside of the binnacle; a Heeling Error Bucket capable of being moved vertically up or down in the centre of the binnacle and which is fitted to hold permanent magnets in a vertical position. The binnacle is also fitted to accommodate fore and aft and athwartship horizontal permanent magnets.

Magnetic Field at the Compass Position. The direction of the ship's magnetic field at the compass position will not necessarily be that due to the direction of the ship's head when building, but will be the resultant of several fields of which the general tendency as indicated in *Figs.* 24 and 24A may or may not preponderate. A part of the ship mass-produced may acquire a magnetic field, the direction of which, when such part is placed in position, may differ considerably from the direction of the field of the rest of the material in the vicinity. Local fields may also be set up in the vicinity of welded parts. The magnetic field due to welding when Direct Current is used is known to lie at right angles to a line joining the electrode and the earth and to follow the same rule as for a current flowing in a wire. One of the most important influences on the ship's field at the compass position is that due to the disposition of Vertical Hard Iron effects in that locality. This is discussed more fully in the next chapter.

The resultant magnetic field of the ship at the position of the compass changes its direction with respect to the compass needle, as well as its value, with every change of direction of the ship's head, consequently the deviation will alter with each change of the direction of the ship's head. This means that any alteration of the direction of the ship's head will not be correctly recorded by an uncorrected compass, a circumstance which, if the deviation were large, might have disastrous consequences especially in crowded waters. The fact that when bearings are taken by the compass the deviation for the particular direction of the ship's head must be allowed for, and also that magnetic courses have to be corrected for deviation to obtain the compass courses to steer and *vice versa*, is a minor consideration.

The ship's field will, on certain ship's heads, be acting more or less with the earth's field, and on others be acting against it. The former condition increases the directive force acting on the compass needle, and the latter decreases the directive force. The increase of directive force is in some respects desirable but the inevitable corresponding decrease is not. Further, in order to ensure reliability of the compass, it is necessary that it should remain in a uniform field in the direction of the magnetic meridian as the ship rotates round it.

The principle underlying the correction of the compass can therefore be stated as follows: *If the directive force at the compass position be equalised on all points of the ship's head in azimuth there will be no deviation on any point, and any alteration of the ship's head in azimuth will be correctly recorded by the compass.*

CHAPTER IX

THE SHIP'S PERMANENT MAGNETISM

In order to compensate for the ship's disturbing magnetic fields the method adopted is to divide the effects into components and then deal with each component separately. The components chosen are those related to the fore and aft, athwartship and vertical directions in the ship through the centre of the compass needle system.

These components are termed the Fore and Aft component, the Athwartship component and the Vertical component of the ship's field respectively, and when considered conjointly are always written and thought of in that particular order. Any force under consideration which is acting at an angle to any of these directions is first divided into two or three of these components. Reference to this method has already been made in Chapter I.

The division of the earth's total force into horizontal and vertical components has also been discussed.

The ship's permanent magnetism may be defined as that part of the ship's magnetism which would remain unaltered if we imagine the ship to be entirely removed from any external field, and in particular the earth's field.

As previously stated, the sub-permanent magnetism of the ship together with that of a lasting nature are treated as permanent for the purposes of correction.

That part of the ship's permanent magnetism acquired due to the influence of the earth's field, if horizontal in direction, may be considered due to the earth's horizontal component H, and that which is vertical may be considered due to the earth's vertical component Z.

The effect due to Z in the northern hemisphere is to cause a blue pole at the upper end of vertical structures and a red pole at the lower end. This reasoning applies, for instance, while the ship is being built and is irrespective of the direction of the ship's head on the stocks or the position of the structure relative to the compass position.

Consider the effect of such a structure on deviation (see *Fig.* 25). The permanent blue pole of the structure will cause an attraction of the north end of the compass needle forward and downward in direction. Two component forces, one horizontal and one vertical (shown dotted in *Fig.* 25), could be substituted for the single force

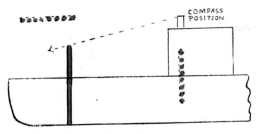

FIG. 25

having exactly the same effect. As the compass card is constrained to the horizontal, the vertical component will have no effect on deviation when the ship is upright. If the structure is in the centre line of the ship, the horizontal component will cause no deviation when the ship is heading north or south by compass, but will cause an easterly deviation on easterly courses and a westerly deviation on westerly courses.

It will thus be realised that the effect of a permanently magnetised vertical structure on deviation is exactly the same as if it were horizontal with its same pole (in this case the blue pole) nearest the compass and its length in the line joining the centre of the compass to the near pole.

The effect of all forces under consideration is measured in terms of the deviation which they cause, thus it is obvious that the amount of vertical permanent magnetism in any direction from the compass position is indeterminate, as the deviation it causes might just as effectively be caused by permanently magnetised horizontal material of the same polarity in the same vicinity.

It is for this reason in particular that the general tendency as to the direction of the ship's magnetic field, discussed in the previous chapter and illustrated in *Figs.* 24 and 24A, may be considerably in error.

Next consider a section of permanently magnetised horizontal material not in the horizontal plane through the compass as in *Fig.* 26 (overleaf).

The near blue pole will cause an attraction of the north end of the compass needle forward and downward in direction. Two component forces, one horizontal and one vertical (shown dotted in *Fig.* 26) could be substituted having exactly the same effect. As before, the vertical component will have no effect on deviation when

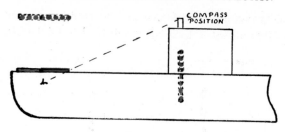

FIG. 26

the ship is upright. If the section is considered fore and aft in the centre line of the ship, the horizontal component will have the same effect on deviation as the fore and aft horizontal component of the vertical structure discussed in the previous example.

The effect, therefore, of the ship's permanent magnetism on deviation is such that, while the ship is upright, the deviation appears to be caused entirely by horizontal permanently magnetised material lying in the horizontal plane through the compass. The vertical effect appears to be due to permanently magnetised vertical material immediately *below* the compass causing heeling error when the ship is inclined from the upright. Strictly speaking, one should say *above* or *below* the compass, through a red pole above the compass can be considered as a blue pole below the compass, and *vice versa.*

The horizontal effects of the permanent magnetism, if not in a fore and aft or in an athwartship direction, must be divided into those two components. The fore and aft component of the horizontal effect is referred to as the *Fore and Aft Component* of the ship's permanent magnetism and is called force P.

Force P is considered positive $(+P)$ when it causes an attraction of the north end of the compass needle toward the bow, and negative $(-P)$ when this attraction is toward the stern.

The athwartship component of the horizontal effect is referred to as the *Athwartship Component* of the ship's permanent magnetism and is called force Q.

Force Q is considered positive $(+Q)$ when it causes an attraction of the north end of the compass needle toward the starboard side, and negative $(-Q)$ when this attraction is to port.

The vertical effect above or blow the compass is referred to as the *Vertical Component* of the ship's permanent magnetism and is called force R.

Force R is considered positive $(+R)$ when it causes an attraction of the north end of the compass needle downward or toward the keel, and negative $(-R)$ when this attraction is upward or toward the mast-head.

The method of determining and using the forces P, Q and R together with the soft-iron effects in the investigation of deviations of the compass is the subject of a later chapter.

CHAPTER X

THE SHIP'S INDUCED MAGNETISM

It has already been stated that there is an effect present at the compass position similar to that which could be caused by magnetically soft iron. The effect is dealt with in a similar manner to that described for the effect of the permanent magnetism in the ship, that is to say, it is divided into a fore and aft, athwartship and vertical component.

The effect is due, however, to induction by the earth's field in soft iron, and the direction of the induction in the material will vary with every change in the direction of the material with reference to the earth's field. In other words, the direction of the induction will change with every change in the direction of the ship's head. This necessitates giving each of the components a fore and aft, athwartship and vertical component to itself, making nine components in all.

It might be argued in this case that the further division into components could go on indefinitely, but this is precluded by defining precisely the components in such a way that all the effects of induction in material of a soft-iron nature are covered by nine such components, no less but no more.

These nine precisely defined components are purely a mathematical device, but it must be stressed that they do cover all the practical effects and are capable of being easily understood.

Each component is considered to be a soft-iron rod without thickness, so that it cannot be magnetised except through its length, and of infinite length, so that only the near end or pole is effective, i.e., able to act on the compass.

Certain of the rods are required to be imagined as passing through the compass position. In this case it will be found that either end may be considered as the near or effective end.

The nine rods are known by the letters a, b, c, d, e, f, g, h and k. They should be thought of in groups of three in the alphabetical order given above.

The first three, a, b and c, are the fore and aft, athwartship and vertical components respectively of the fore and aft horizontal component of the ship's induced magnetic field. Consequently each

of the rods must have its near or effective end in the fore and aft
horizontal plane through the compass and also, by virtue of the

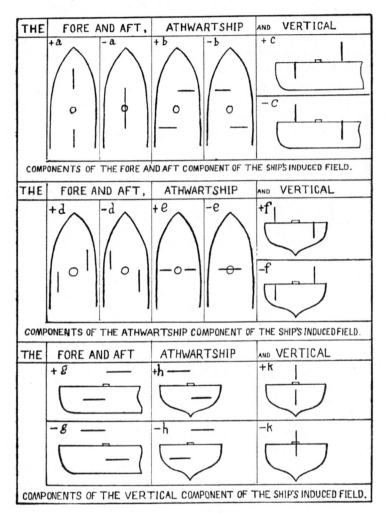

THE NINE RODS.

definition, a must be a fore and aft rod, b must be an athwartship
rod, and c a vertical rod.

The second or middle group of three rods, d, e and f, are the
fore and aft, athwartship and vertical components respectively of the
athwartship horizontal component of the ship's induced magnetic

field. Consequently, each of the rods must have its near or effective end in the athwartship plane through the compass and, by virtue of the definition, d must be a fore and aft rod, e an athwartship rod, and f a vertical rod.

The last three rods, g, h and k, are the fore and aft, athwartship and vertical components respectively of the vertical component of the ship's induced magnetic field. Consequently, each of the rods must have its near or effective end vertically above or below the compass position and, by virtue of the definition, g must be a fore and aft rod, h must be an athwartship rod, and k a vertical rod.

The foregoing Table of diagrams indicates the positions of the various rods with reference to the compass position. Although alternative positions are given and a positive or negative sign is attached to each, it must be emphasised that the rods represent effects and as such there need be considered but one of each of the rods in the ship. Which of the alternative positions is used is immaterial providing the sign is right. The method of determining the sign of a rod is simple, as will be seen from the explanation which follows below.

There is no need to memorise the Table, remember that the rods are components, that the order is always "fore and aft, athwartships and vertical" in groups of three alphabetically arranged with i and j omitted. Incidentally, it is much easier to keep all the nine rods in mind than to single out only those which appear normally at the position of a well-placed compass.

To Determine the Algebraic Signs of the Various Rods. It will be remembered that in the case of a ship's permanent magnetism it was shown that an attraction forward or to the bow was positive, an attraction to starboard was positive and an attraction downward or toward the keel was positive, while an attraction aft, to port or upward was considered negative.

In the case of the rods it is convenient to remember simply that "forward is plus, to starboard is plus and downward is plus", while aft, to port or upward are negative.

Consider the direction of the near end of each rod from the compass position and apply the appropriate sign ($+$ or $-$), then consider the direction of the far end of each rod to its near-end position and apply the appropriate sign ($+$ or $-$). The "product" of the signs thus obtained will give the correct sign for each particular rod.

Take, for example, the two positions of the $+a$ rod given in the Table and reproduced in *Fig.* 27.

First the rod in its forward position: the near
end of the rod is forward of the compass and is
therefore +, the far end is forward of the near
end and is therefore +, and plus times a plus
is positive. The rod is a $+a$ rod.

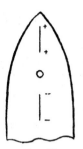

FIG. 27

Next the rod in its after position: the near end
is aft of the compass and is −, the far end is aft
of the near end and is also −, and minus times
a minus is positive. The rod is a $+a$ rod as before.
A rod in either of these positions would have
the same effect on the compass.

Again, for example, take the $-e$ rod as shown in the Table and
reproduced in *Fig.* 28. It is continuous right through the compass

position and either end may be considered the
near end. First let us assume that the starboard
end is the near end; it is to starboard of the
compass and therefore +, the other end is to
port of the near end and therefore −, and plus
times a minus is negative. The rod is a $-e$
rod. Alternatively, assume that the port end is
the near end; then it is to port of the compass
and −, the other end is then to starboard of
the near end and +, and minus times a plus is
negative. The rod is again a $-e$ rod.

FIG. 28

It should be noted that only three of the rods can be continuous
through the compass position. They are the first of the first group,
the second of the second group and the third of the third group,
that is a, e and k respectively, and in each case, if continuous, the
rod is negative.

Let us now pick any rod at random and fully identify it without
reference to the Table.

Figure 29 shows a vertical rod to port of the
compass. Its near end is in the athwartship plane
through the compass, the rod must therefore, be
one of the middle group, either d, e or f, but
as it is vertical it must be the last of the three,
i.e., an f rod. The near end is to port of the
compass and, therefore, −, the far end is above
the near end and is also −, and minus times a
minus is positive. The rod is a plus f rod.

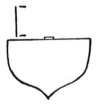

FIG. 29

Now let us put say a $-g$ rod in the ship. Going through the
alphabet we find it is in the third or last of the groups of three. Its

near end must therefore be vertically above or below the compass position, and as it is the first of the three (*g*, *h* and *k*), it is fore and aft in direction. Whether we put it above or below the compass is immaterial providing the product of the signs is negative, which means that the two ends must be of opposite sign.

If the near end is placed vertically below the compass its sign will be positive and the other end, the far end, must be in the negative direction that is aft of the near end as in *Fig.* 30.

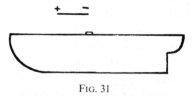

FIG. 30

If the near end is placed vertically above the compass its sign will be negative and the other end, the far end, must be in the positive direction that is forward of the near end as in *Fig.* 31.

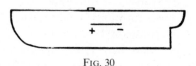

FIG. 31

Practical Application. Consider the soft-iron effects of a derrick stepped in the middle line of a ship on the fore deck and elevated in the fore and aft line at an angle to the horizontal so that the head of the derrick is aft of its heel and slightly below and forward of the compass position as shown diagrammatically in *Fig.* 32.

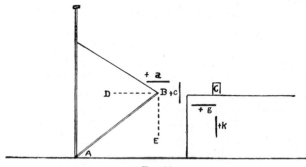

FIG. 32

The derrick *BA* in *Fig.* 32 will have a horizontal and vertical component, *BD* and *BE* respectively.

The effective end of *BD*, the horizontal component, which is fore and aft, acts in a forward and downward direction from the compass position *C* in *Fig. 32*.

This effect requires two fore and aft horizontal rods, one with its near end immediately forward of the compass and one with its near end immediately below the compass, the former will be seen to be a $+a$ rod and the latter a $+g$ rod.

The effective end of *BE*, the vertical component, also acts in a forward and downward direction from the compass position.

This effect requires two vertical rods, one with its near end immediately forward of the compass and one with its near end immediately below the compass, the former will be seen to be a $+c$ rod and the latter a $+k$ rod.

Thus the soft-iron effects of the derrick on the compass would be equivalent to the combined effects of four rods, *i.e.*, $+a$, $+c$, $+g$ and $+k$.

The nine rods together with the forces *P*, *Q* and *R* are the derivatives of the Coefficients which determine the type of deviation that any combination of forces and rods may cause. The method by which the coefficients are determined is the subject of the next chapter.

CHAPTER XI

THE THEORY OF THE DEVIATIONS OF
THE COMPASS

THE direction of the earth's horizontal force H at the compass position relative to the fore and aft line will vary with every change of the ship's head. It is necessary therefore to give it a fore and aft component X and an athwartship component Y. The vertical component is, of course, Z.

The fore and aft rods a, d and g will derive their respective force from induction by X. These forces can be considered equal to aX, dX and gX respectively where a, d and g are constant quantities depending on the magnetic qualities of soft iron such as permeability.

The athwartship rods b, e and h will derive their respective forces from induction by Y. These forces can be considered equal to bY, eY and hY respectively where b, e and h are constants as above.

Similarly, the vertical rods c, f and k will derive their respective forces from induction from Z. These forces can be considered equal to cZ, fZ and kZ respectively.

The total magnetic force at the compass position due to the effect of all the forces present may be written H'. This must be divided into three components also, the fore and aft component is X', the athwartship component is Y' and the vertical component is Z'. X', Y' and Z' are considered positive when the force is directed toward the bow, the starboard side and toward the keel respectively.

This total magnetic force is made up of:

(1) The magnetic force due to the earth, X, Y and Z, positive to the bow, starboard side and keel respectively.

(2) The magnetic force due to the permanent magnetism of the ship, P, Q and R, positive to the bow, starboard side and keel respectively.

(3) The magnetic force due to induction in the soft-iron rods comprising the fore and aft component $(aX + bY + cZ)$, positive if directed toward the bow, the athwartship component $(dX + eY + fZ)$, positive if directed toward the starboard side, and the vertical component $(gX + hY + kZ)$, positive if directed toward the keel.

Note. The positive signs used in the above expressions merely indicate the algebraic sum of the quantities, each expression being in its general form. For any specific case, the signs being known, they may be inserted without altering the sense of the expression. For instance, if in the expression $(aX + bY + cZ)$ it is known that a and c are positive but b is negative, the expression then becomes $[aX + (-bY) + cZ]$ or $(aX - bY + cZ)$.

From (1), (2) and (3) above we can write the following three equations:

$$X' = X + aX + bY + cZ + P \qquad (1)$$
$$Y' = Y + dX + eY + fZ + Q \qquad (2)$$
$$Z' = Z + gX + hY + kZ + R \qquad (3)$$

These are the three fundamental equations on which the whole theory is based.

Equation 1 is the total magnetic force acting toward the bow (because X' is written positive), and it will be seen that it includes all the forces that act in the fore and aft line.

Equation 2 is the total magnetic force acting toward the starboard side (because Y' is written positive), and it will be seen that it includes all the forces that act in the athwartship direction through the compass position.

Equation 3 is the total magnetic force acting toward the keel (because Z' is written positive), and it includes all the forces that act in a vertical direction through the compass position.

These three fundamental equations are simple in form and obviously true but are just as obviously of no use to the navigator or adjuster, who requires to know what deviations the various forces will cause and what effect change of direction of ship's head will have.

By mathematical manipulation of the equations we can obtain the results we require.

First, consider for a moment the components X and Y of the earth's horizontal force H acting at the compass position with the ship heading in a north-easterly direction (*Fig.* 33).

Let the magnetic course be ζ (zeta). X is acting toward the bow and is positive, while Y is acting to port and is conventionally, but not trigonometrically, negative.

From the triangle of forces we get

$$\frac{X}{H} = \cos \zeta$$

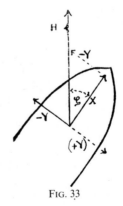

FIG. 33

$$\therefore \qquad X = H \cos \zeta.$$

Also $\qquad \dfrac{-Y}{H} = \sin \zeta$

and therefore $\quad -Y = H \sin \zeta$

from which $\qquad Y = -H \sin \zeta$

where $-H \sin \zeta$ is directed toward the starboard side. (See Chapter II, p. 10, last paragraph.)

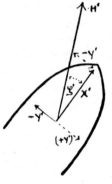

Similar reasoning applies to the components X' and Y' of the ship's total magnetic force H' (see *Fig.* 34), the ship still assumed to be heading in a north-easterly direction.

Let the compass course be ζ' (zeta "dash"). Then from the triangle of forces we get

$$X' = H' \cos \zeta'$$

and also $\quad -Y' = H' \sin \zeta'$

therefore $\quad Y' = -H' \sin \zeta'$

FIG. 34

where $-H' \zeta'$ is the total force directed to the starboard side.

Figure 35 represents the ship heading in a north-easterly direction. Let the ship's head magnetic (Magnetic Course) be ζ, *i.e.*, the angle between the fore and aft line through the compass and the direction of the earth's horizontal force H.

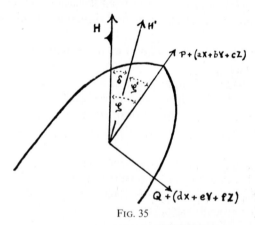

FIG. 35

Let the ship's head compass (Compass Course) be ζ', *i.e.*, the angle between the fore and aft line through the compass and the direction of the resultant force at the compass position H'.

Then $\zeta - \zeta' = \delta$ the deviation for the direction of the ship's head, for if ζ' is the greater δ will be negative or westerly.

Substituting in equations 1 and 2, $H \cos \zeta$ for X, $-H \sin \zeta$ for Y, $H' \cos \zeta'$ for X' and $-H' \sin \zeta'$ for Y'

then equation 1 becomes

$$H' \cos \zeta' = H \cos \zeta + aH \cos \zeta - bH \sin \zeta + cZ + P$$

and equation 2 becomes

$$-H' \sin \zeta' = -H \sin \zeta + dH \cos \zeta - eH \sin \zeta + fZ + Q.$$

Divide each side of each equation by H, this will in no way alter the values, and also remember that

$$\frac{Z}{H} = \tan \theta,$$

where $\theta = $ the angle of Dip. Thus we get

$$\frac{H'}{H} \cos \zeta' = \cos \zeta + a \cos \zeta - b \sin \zeta + c \tan \theta + \frac{P}{H}$$

and

$$\frac{-H'}{H} \sin \zeta' = -\sin \zeta + d \cos \zeta - e \sin \zeta + f \tan \theta + \frac{Q}{H}.$$

Collecting the cosines in 1 and the sines in 2, we can rewrite the equations as follows:

$$\frac{H'}{H} \cos \zeta' = (1 + a) \cos \zeta - b \sin \zeta + c \tan \theta + \frac{P}{H} \qquad (4)$$

$$\frac{-H'}{H} \sin \zeta' = d \cos \zeta - (1 + e) \sin \zeta + f \tan \theta + \frac{Q}{H}. \qquad (5)$$

Equations 4 and 5 give the total magnetic force toward the bow and to the starboard side respectively in terms of H as the unit where H is in electro-magnetic units. We require these forces, however, in terms of deviation caused and direction of ship's head.

If we multiply both sides of equation 4 by $\sin \zeta$ and both sides of equation 5 by $\cos \zeta$ and add the results together, we get equation 6 below.

Also, if we multiply both sides of equation 4 by $\cos \zeta$ and both sides of equation 5 by $\sin \zeta$ and subtract one equation from the other, we get equation 7 below.

Note. This manipulation in no way alters the mathematical exactness of the expressions.

The full mathematical process used in evolving equations 6 and 7 is given in the next chapter. As all the steps have been included it is, though simple, rather a long process, and may be studied independently if the results here given are temporarily taken for granted.

For the multiplication and addition we get

$$\frac{H'}{H} \sin \delta = \frac{d-b}{2} + \left(c \tan \theta + \frac{P}{H} \right) \sin \zeta + \left(f \tan \theta + \frac{Q}{H} \right) \cos \zeta$$

$$+ \frac{a-e}{2} \sin 2\zeta + \frac{d+b}{2} \cos 2\zeta \qquad (6)$$

For the multiplication and subtraction we get

$$\frac{H'}{H} \cos \delta = \left(1 + \frac{a+e}{2} \right) + \left(c \tan \theta + \frac{P}{H} \right) \cos \zeta - \left(f \tan \theta + \frac{Q}{H} \right)$$

$$\times \sin \zeta + \frac{a-e}{2} \cos 2\zeta - \frac{d+b}{2} \sin 2\zeta \qquad (7)$$

Equations 6 and 7 give the total magnetic force to Magnetic East and to Magnetic North respectively in terms of H as unit.

This will be seen to be true if *Fig.* 36 is referred to, in which *OH* is the direction of Magnetic North from the compass position *O* and *OH'* is the direction of Compass North.

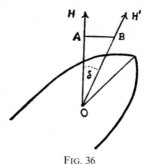

FIG. 36

Let *OB* in *OH'* be the vector sum or resultant of the forces acting at the compass position. From *B* draw *BA* perpendicular to *OH*, cutting *OH* in *A*. Then *OA* represents the vector component of the total force acting in the direction of Magnetic North and *AB* represents the vector component of the total force acting in the direction of Magnetic East (since *AB* is perpendicular to *OA*). The angle *AOB* is the deviation (δ) for the direction of the ship's head, hence $\dfrac{AB}{OB}$ = sin δ and $AB = OB$ sin δ. But $OB = H'$. Therefore

the total force to Magnetic East is H' sin δ and in terms of H as unit

$= \dfrac{H'}{H}$ sin δ (see equation 6).

Similarly, $AO = H'$ cos δ, and the total force to Magnetic North

in terms of H as unit is therefore $\dfrac{H'}{H}$ cos δ (see equation 7).

If we rewrite equations 6 and 7 in the following form:

$$H' \sin \delta = H\left[\frac{d-b}{2} + \left(c \tan \theta + \frac{P}{H}\right)\sin \zeta + \left(f \tan \theta + \frac{Q}{H}\right)\right.$$

$$\left. \times \cos \zeta + \frac{a-e}{2}\sin 2\zeta + \frac{d+b}{2}\cos 2\zeta\right] \quad (6')$$

$$H' \cos \delta = H\left[1 + \frac{a+e}{2} + \left(c \tan \theta + \frac{P}{H}\right)\cos \zeta - \left(f \tan \theta + \frac{Q}{H}\right)\right.$$

$$\left. \times \sin \zeta + \frac{a-e}{2}\cos 2\zeta - \frac{d+b}{2}\sin 2\zeta\right] \quad (7')$$

then 6' and 7' give the total magnetic force to Magnetic East and North respectively.

Before proceeding further let us analyse the terms included in equations 6 and 7.

$\dfrac{d-b}{2}$ (equation 6). This expression is a constant quantity on all courses and in all latitudes. It does not vary with change of course or with change of Dip or H. It is the mean value of $\dfrac{H'}{H}$ sin δ on all points of the ship's head in azimuth as will be clear from the following reasoning:

It will be seen that in equation 6 the expressions following $\dfrac{d-b}{2}$ vary as sin ζ, cos ζ, sin 2ζ and cos 2ζ respectively. The mean value of the sine for all angles from $0°$ to $360°$ is zero; for instance take the four equidistant cardinal points, sin $0° = 0$, sin $90° = 1$, sin $180° = 0$, and sin $270° = -1$, the mean being $\dfrac{0+1+0-1}{4} = 0$.

Similarly, the mean value of the cosine for all angles from 0° to 360° is zero. Using the four cardinal points again we get $\dfrac{1 + 0 - 1 + 0}{4} = 0$. Sin 2ζ and cos 2ζ simply involve two resolutions

and the result is again zero. Hence the mean value of $\dfrac{H'}{H} \sin \delta$

for all headings of the ship in azimuth is $\dfrac{d - b}{2}$.

Note. When a number of equidistant points are taken to verify the above it is obvious that, short of the infinite, an even number of points must be used in order that there shall be pairs of points diametrically opposed to one another.

$c \tan \theta + \dfrac{P}{H}$. This part of both equations is not a constant; in equation 6 it varies as sin ζ with change of ship's head, and in equation 7 it varies as cos ζ. It is thus a semicircular part of the deviation. Referring back to the equation 4 (p. 69), it will be realised that it is also the mean value of the total magnetic force toward the bow. $c \tan \theta$ arises from induction by the earth's vertical field in the symmetrically disposed soft iron, about the centre line, forward or abaft the compass. "c" depends for its sign on whether the excess is forward or abaft the compass position and varies directly as the tangent of the Dip. "P" varies inversely as H.

$f \tan \theta + \dfrac{Q}{H}$. This part of both equations is not a constant; in equation 6 it varies as cos ζ with change of ship's head, and in equation 7 it varies as sin ζ. It is thus a semicircular part of the deviation. Referring back to equation 5 (p. 69), it will be realised that it is also the mean value of the total magnetic force toward the starboard side. $f \tan \theta$ arises from induction by the earth's vertical field in the soft iron disposed to starboard or port of the compass position. "f" depends for its sign on whether the excess is to starboard or port of the compass position and varies directly as the tangent of the Dip. "Q" varies inversely as H.

$\dfrac{a - e}{2}$. This expression varies in equation 6 as sin 2ζ and in equation 7 as cos 2ζ; it is, therefore, a quadrantal part of the deviation which changes its sign in alternate quadrants with change of direction of the ship's head in azimuth. It does not vary, however, with change of value of H or of Dip, and is, therefore, constant in sign and amount in all latitudes for any particular value of 2ζ. It arises from induction by the earth's horizontal field in soft iron symmetrically disposed about the fore and aft or athwartship planes through the compass position.

$\dfrac{d + b}{2}$. This expression varies in equation 6 as $\cos 2\zeta$ and in equation 7 as $\sin 2\zeta$; it is therefore a quadrantal part of the deviation, and as in the case of $\dfrac{a - e}{2}$, it is constant in sign and amount in all latitudes for any particular direction of the ship's head. It arises from induction by the earth's horizontal field in soft iron which is *not* symmetrically disposed about the fore and aft or about the athwartship plane through the compass position.

$1 + \dfrac{a + e}{2}$ (equation 7). This expression is a constant quantity and does not vary with change of course or change of latitude and, using the same reasoning as for $\dfrac{d - b}{2}$ in equation 6, it will be seen that it is the mean value of $\dfrac{H'}{H} \cos \delta$ for all points of the ship's head in azimuth. Now it has been shown that equation 7 gives the total magnetic force toward Magnetic North at the compass position (see p. 70). It can therefore be stated that the expression $1 + \dfrac{a + e}{2}$ is the mean directive force toward Magnetic North at the compass position in terms of H, the earth's horizontal force, as the unit of measurement. This value is important, and it should be realised that it depends on induction by the earth's horizontal field in soft iron symmetrically disposed about the fore and aft or athwartship planes through the compass position.

The remaining terms in equation 7 have already been discussed.

Equations 6 and 7 are interdependent as they both, with the exception of their constant terms, contain the same terms, nor do they give us the deviation explicitly in terms of the course. We must therefore proceed further.

In order to curtail the length of the expressions we can give each of the terms a name.

Therefore let $1 + \dfrac{a + e}{2} = \lambda$ (lambda)

$$\frac{d - b}{2\lambda} = \overline{A}$$

$$\frac{1}{\lambda}\left(c \tan\theta + \frac{P}{H}\right) = \bar{B}$$

$$\frac{1}{\lambda}\left(f \tan\theta + \frac{Q}{H}\right) = \bar{C}$$

$$\frac{a - e}{2\lambda} = \bar{D}$$

$$\frac{d + b}{2\lambda} = \bar{E}$$

$\bar{A}, \bar{B}, \bar{C}, \bar{D}$ and $\bar{E}$ are called the *Exact Coefficients*. It should be noted that each of the terms from which the exact coefficients are derived has been divided by λ. This is necessary, as obviously any expression we are able to evolve giving us the deviation explicitly must vary inversely as the directive force. Therefore in rewriting equations 6 and 7, using the exact coefficients, the remaining terms must also be divided by λ.

Equation 6 then becomes

$$\frac{H'}{H\lambda} \sin\delta = \bar{A} + \bar{B}\sin\zeta + \bar{C}\cos\zeta + \bar{D}\sin 2\zeta + \bar{E}\cos 2\zeta \quad (8)$$

Equation 7 becomes

$$\frac{H'}{H\lambda} \cos\delta = 1 + \bar{B}\cos\zeta - \bar{C}\sin\zeta + \bar{D}\cos 2\zeta - \bar{E}\sin 2\zeta \quad (9)$$

If we divide equation 8 by equation 9, $\dfrac{H'}{H\lambda}$ cancels, also $\dfrac{\sin\delta}{\cos\delta}$

$= \tan\delta$ and we get

$$\text{Tan } \delta = \frac{\bar{A} + \bar{B}\sin\zeta + \bar{C}\cos\zeta + \bar{D}\sin 2\zeta + \bar{E}\cos 2\zeta}{1 + \bar{B}\cos\zeta - \bar{C}\sin\zeta + \bar{D}\cos 2\zeta - \bar{E}\sin 2\zeta} \quad (10)$$

Equation 10 gives the deviation explicitly in terms of the Magnetic Course when the exact coefficients are known.

The Coefficients $\lambda, \bar{A}, \bar{B}, \bar{C}, \bar{D}$ and $\bar{E}$.

(λ) $$\lambda = 1 + \frac{a + e}{2}$$

It has already been shown (p. 71) that $H' \cos\delta$ is a measure of the directive force to Magnetic North for any particular direction of the ship's head. Also, from equation 7, the mean value of $\dfrac{H'}{H} \cos \delta = \lambda$,

therefore the mean value of $H' \cos \delta = \lambda H$.

λH is the mean directive force to Magnetic North for all headings of the ship.

λ is therefore the ratio of the mean directive force at the compass position compared with H the earth's horizontal force at the place.

$(\bar{D})$ $$\bar{D} = \frac{a - e}{2\lambda}.$$

$\bar{D}$ is a coefficient of quadrantal deviation and is constant in name and amount in all latitudes for any particular direction of the ship's head.

The usual values of λ and $\bar{D}$ are, in practice, such as would be given by an arrangement of $-a$ and $-e$ rods, the $-e$ rod having the greater effect. This is the effect that would be obtained from longitudinal and transverse bulkheads running the full length and breadth of the ship, the induced magnetic poles of the latter being nearer the compass.

Substituting the above signs in the expression for λ we get

$$\lambda = 1 + \frac{(-a - e)}{2} = 1 - \frac{a + e}{2}$$

from which we see that the value of λ will be less than unity; it is, however, always positive.

For $\bar{D}$ we get

$$\bar{D} = \frac{-a - (-e)}{2\lambda} = \frac{-a + e}{2\lambda}$$

and, e being the greater, $\bar{D}$ will be positive.

The soft-iron correcting spheres have the effect of $+e$ rods, and serve to correct a positive value of $\bar{D}$ and also to increase the value of the directive force λH.

$(\bar{A} \text{ and } \bar{E})$ $$\bar{A} = \frac{d - b}{2\lambda}, \qquad \bar{E} = \frac{d + b}{2\lambda}.$$

It has already been shown that $\bar{A}$ is the coefficient of the constant part of the deviation and that $\bar{E}$ is a coefficient of quadrantal deviation. Neither vary with change of magnetic latitude. When the soft iron of the ship is symmetrically placed with reference to a

D

fore and aft vertical plane through the compass position, the values of the d and b rods will be zero. Consequently $\overline{A}$ and $\overline{E}$ will be zero. This is usually so when the compass is placed on the fore and aft centre line of the ship, but in any case a compass position can normally be found where the values of $\overline{A}$ and $\overline{E}$ are small.

($\overline{B}$)
$$\overline{B} = \frac{1}{\lambda}\left(c \tan \theta + \frac{P}{H}\right).$$

$\overline{B}$ is a coefficient of semicircular deviation. Earlier in this chapter it was seen that the total magnetic force acting toward the bow X' was equal to $H' \cos \zeta'$. From equation 4 we see that the mean value of

$$H' \cos \zeta' = \left(c \tan \theta + \frac{P}{H}\right)H,$$

hence $\lambda H\overline{B}$ is the mean value of the total force toward the bow for all headings of the ship.

($\overline{C}$)
$$\overline{C} = \frac{1}{\lambda}\left(f \tan \theta + \frac{Q}{H}\right).$$

$\overline{C}$ is a coefficient of semicircular deviation. Using the same reasoning as for $\overline{B}$ above, from equation 5 we see that the mean value of

$$H' \sin \zeta' = \left(f \tan \theta + \frac{Q}{H}\right)H,$$

hence $\lambda H\overline{C}$ is the mean value of the total force to starboard for all headings of the ship. Normally vertical induction in soft iron is equally divided to port and starboard of the fore and aft centre line, and if the compass is placed on this line the value of the f rod effect will be negligible, and $f \tan \theta$ will be zero.

If $f \tan \theta = 0$, then $\overline{C} = \dfrac{Q}{\lambda H}$.

Equation 10 is a cumbersome expression to use. Its chief disadvantage is that it gives the deviation in terms of the Magnetic Course, whereas it would be much more convenient to the navigator or compass adjuster to have an equation for deviation in terms of the Compass Course. This aspect is discussed in Chapter XIII following and such an expression is found.

CHAPTER XII

TRANSFORMATION OF EQUATIONS (4) AND (5)

$$\frac{H'}{H}\cos\zeta' = (1+a)\cos\zeta - b\sin\zeta + c\tan\theta + \frac{P}{H}$$
(4). Multiply by $\sin\zeta$.

$$\frac{H'}{H}\cos\zeta'\sin\zeta = (1+a)\cos\zeta\sin\zeta - b\sin^2\zeta + c\tan\theta\sin\zeta + \frac{P}{H}\sin\zeta$$
(4′).

$$-\frac{H'}{H}\sin\zeta' = d\cos\zeta - (1+e)\sin\zeta + f\tan\theta + \frac{Q}{H}$$
(5). Multiply by $\cos\zeta$.

$$-\frac{H'}{H}\sin\zeta'\cos\zeta = d\cos^2\zeta - (1+e)\sin\zeta\cos\zeta + f\tan\theta\cos\zeta + \frac{Q}{H}\cos\zeta$$
(5′).

Adding (4′) and (5′) together and rearranging some of the terms we get

$$\frac{H'}{H}\sin\zeta\cos\zeta' - \frac{H'}{H}\cos\zeta\sin\zeta' = \left(c\tan\theta + \frac{P}{H}\right)\sin\zeta + \left(f\tan\theta + \frac{Q}{H}\right)\cos\zeta + d\cos^2\zeta - b\sin^2\zeta + (1+a)\sin\zeta\cos\zeta - (1+e)\sin\zeta\cos\zeta$$

$$\frac{H'}{H}(\sin\zeta\cos\zeta' - \cos\zeta\sin\zeta') = \left(c\tan\theta + \frac{P}{H}\right)\sin\zeta + \left(f\tan\theta + \frac{Q}{H}\right)\cos\zeta + (1+a-1-e)\sin\zeta\cos\zeta + \frac{d}{2}2\cos^2\zeta - \frac{b}{2}2\sin^2\zeta$$

$$\frac{H'}{H}\sin(\zeta-\zeta')* = \left(c\tan\theta + \frac{P}{H}\right)\sin\zeta + \left(f\tan\theta + \frac{Q}{H}\right)\cos\zeta + \frac{a-e}{2}2\sin\zeta\cos\zeta + \frac{d}{2}[(1+\cos^2\zeta)-(1-\cos^2\zeta)]† - \frac{b}{2}[(1+\sin^2\zeta)-(1-\sin^2\zeta)]$$

$$\frac{H'}{H}\sin\delta = \left(c\tan\theta + \frac{P}{H}\right)\sin\zeta + (f\tan\theta + \frac{Q}{H})\cos\zeta + \frac{a-e}{2}\sin 2\zeta‡ + \frac{d}{2} + \frac{d}{2}\cos^2\zeta - \frac{d}{2}\sin^2\zeta - \frac{b}{2} - \frac{b}{2}\sin^2\zeta + \frac{b}{2}\cos^2\zeta$$

$$\frac{H'}{H}\sin\delta = \left(c\tan\theta + \frac{P}{H}\right)\sin\zeta + \left(f\tan\theta + \frac{Q}{H}\right)\cos\zeta + \frac{a-e}{2}\sin 2\zeta + \frac{d-b}{2} + \frac{d}{2}(\cos^2\zeta - \sin^2\zeta) + \frac{b}{2}(\cos^2\zeta - \sin^2\zeta)$$

$$\frac{H'}{H}\sin\delta = \left(c\tan\theta + \frac{P}{H}\right)\sin\zeta + \left(f\tan\theta + \frac{Q}{H}\right)\cos\zeta + \frac{a-e}{2}\sin 2\zeta + \frac{d-b}{2} + \frac{d+b}{2}(\cos^2\zeta - \sin^2\zeta)$$

$$\frac{H'}{H}\sin\delta = \left(c\tan\theta + \frac{P}{H}\right)\sin\zeta + \left(f\tan\theta + \frac{Q}{H}\right)\cos\zeta + \frac{a-e}{2}\sin 2\zeta + \frac{d-b}{2} + \frac{d+b}{2}\cos 2\zeta§$$

$$\frac{H'}{H}\sin\delta = \frac{d-b}{2} + \left(c\tan\theta + \frac{P}{H}\right)\sin\zeta + \left(f\tan\theta + \frac{Q}{H}\right)\cos\zeta + \frac{a-e}{2}\sin 2\zeta + \frac{d+b}{2}\cos 2\zeta$$
(6).

* See equation 3, page 18.
† $2\cos^2\zeta = \cos^2\zeta + \cos^2\zeta$, add and subtract $1 = (1+\cos^2\zeta) - (1-\cos^2\zeta)$ and $(1-\cos^2\zeta) = \sin^2\zeta$.
‡ See equation 9, page 18.   § See equation 10, page 18.

$$\frac{H'}{H}\cos\zeta' = (1+a)\cos\zeta - b\sin\zeta + c\tan\theta + \frac{P}{H}$$

(4). Multiply by $\cos\zeta$.

$$\frac{H'}{H}\cos\zeta'\cos\zeta = (1+a)\cos^2\zeta - b\sin\zeta\cos\zeta + c\tan\theta\cos\zeta + \frac{P}{H}\cos\zeta$$

(4″).

$$-\frac{H'}{H}\sin\zeta' = d\cos\zeta - (1+e)\sin\zeta + f\tan\theta + \frac{Q}{H}$$

(5). Multiply by $\sin\zeta$.

$$-\frac{H'}{H}\sin\zeta'\sin\zeta = d\sin\zeta\cos\zeta - (1+e)\sin^2\zeta + f\tan\theta\sin\zeta + \frac{Q}{H}\sin\zeta$$

(5″).

Subtracting (5″) from (4″) by changing the signs in (5″) and some rearrangement we get

$$\frac{H'}{H}\cos\zeta\cos\zeta' + \frac{H'}{H}\sin\zeta\sin\zeta' = \left(c\tan\theta + \frac{P}{H}\right)\cos\zeta - \left(f\tan\theta + \frac{Q}{H}\right)\sin\zeta - b\sin\zeta\cos\zeta - d\sin\zeta\cos\zeta + (1+a)\cos^2\zeta + (1+e)$$
$$\times\ \sin^2\zeta$$

$$\frac{H'}{H}(\cos\zeta\cos\zeta' + \sin\zeta\sin\zeta') = \left(c\tan\theta + \frac{P}{H}\right)\cos\zeta - \left(f\tan\theta + \frac{Q}{H}\right)\sin\zeta - (b+d)\sin\zeta\cos\zeta + \frac{1+a}{2}2\cos^2\zeta + \frac{1+e}{2}2\sin^2\zeta$$

$$\frac{H'}{H}\cos(\zeta-\zeta')^* = \left(c\tan\theta + \frac{P}{H}\right)\cos\zeta - \left(f\tan\theta + \frac{Q}{H}\right)\sin\zeta - \frac{b+d}{2}2\sin\zeta\cos\zeta + \frac{1+a}{2}[(1+\cos^2\zeta)-(1-\cos^2\zeta)] + \frac{1+e}{2}$$
$$\times\ [(1+\sin^2\zeta)-(1-\sin^2\zeta)]\dagger$$

$$\frac{H'}{H}\cos\delta = \left(c\tan\theta + \frac{P}{H}\right)\cos\zeta - \left(f\tan\theta + \frac{Q}{H}\right)\sin\zeta - \frac{b+d}{2}\sin 2\zeta\ddagger + \frac{1+a}{2} + \frac{1+a}{2}\cos^2\zeta - \frac{1+a}{2}\sin^2\zeta + \frac{1+e}{2} + \frac{1+e}{2}\sin^2\zeta - \frac{1+e}{2}\cos^2\zeta$$

$$\frac{H'}{H}\cos\delta = \left(c\tan\theta + \frac{P}{H}\right)\cos\zeta - \left(f\tan\theta + \frac{Q}{H}\right)\sin\zeta - \frac{b+d}{2}\sin 2\zeta + \frac{1+a+1+e}{2} + \frac{1+a}{2}(\cos^2\zeta - \sin^2\zeta) - \frac{1+e}{2}(\cos^2\zeta - \sin^2\zeta)$$

$$\frac{H'}{H}\cos\delta = \left(c\tan\theta + \frac{P}{H}\right)\cos\zeta - \left(f\tan\theta + \frac{Q}{H}\right)\sin\zeta - \frac{b+d}{2}\sin 2\zeta + 1 + \frac{a+e}{2} + \frac{1+a-1-e}{2}(\cos^2\zeta - \sin^2\zeta)$$

$$\frac{H'}{H}\cos\delta = \left(c\tan\theta + \frac{P}{H}\right)\cos\zeta - \left(f\tan\theta + \frac{Q}{H}\right)\sin\zeta - \frac{b+d}{2}\sin 2\zeta + 1 + \frac{a+e}{2} + \frac{a-e}{2}\cos 2\zeta\ \S$$

$$\frac{H'}{H}\cos\delta = 1 + \frac{a+e}{2} + \left(c\tan\theta + \frac{P}{H}\right)\cos\zeta - \left(f\tan\theta + \frac{Q}{H}\right)\sin\zeta + \frac{a+e}{2}\cos 2\zeta - \frac{b+d}{2}\sin 2\zeta$$

(7).

* See equation 4, page 18.
† $2\sin^2\zeta = \sin^2\zeta + \sin^2\zeta$, adding and subtracting 1 we get $(1+\sin^2\zeta)-(1-\sin^2\zeta)$, we can therefore write
$$+\frac{1+e}{2}(\sin^2\zeta - \cos^2\zeta)\ \text{or,}\ -\frac{1+e}{2}(\cos^2\zeta - \sin^2\zeta),\ \text{(see two lines below)}.$$

‡ See equation 9, page 18.   § See equation 10, page 18.

78

CHAPTER XIII

DEVIATION IN TERMS OF THE COMPASS COURSE

IF in equation 10 we write $\dfrac{\sin \delta}{\cos \delta}$ for tan δ the equation becomes

$$\frac{\text{Sin } \delta}{\text{Cos } \delta} = \frac{\bar{A} + \bar{B} \sin \zeta + \bar{C} \cos \zeta + \bar{D} \sin 2\zeta + \bar{E} \cos 2\zeta}{1 + \bar{B} \cos \zeta - \bar{C} \sin \zeta + \bar{D} \cos 2\zeta - \bar{E} \sin 2\zeta}.$$

Cross multiplying we get

Sin $\delta + \bar{B} \cos \zeta \sin \delta - \bar{C} \sin \zeta \sin \delta + \bar{D} \cos 2\zeta \sin \delta - \bar{E} \sin 2\zeta \sin \delta$
$= \bar{A} \cos \delta + \bar{B} \sin \zeta \cos \delta + \bar{C} \cos \zeta \cos \delta + \bar{D} \sin 2\zeta \cos \delta$
$+ \bar{E} \cos 2\zeta \cos \delta.$

Shifting all the terms except sin δ to the right-hand side we get

Sin $\delta = \bar{A} \cos \delta + \bar{B} \sin \zeta \cos \delta - \bar{B} \cos \zeta \sin \delta + \bar{C} \cos \zeta \cos \delta$
$+ \bar{C} \sin \zeta \sin \delta + \bar{D} \sin 2\zeta \cos \delta - \bar{D} \cos 2\zeta \sin \zeta$
$+ \bar{E} \cos 2\zeta \cos \delta + \bar{E} \sin 2\zeta \sin \delta.$

Collecting terms we get

Sin $\delta = \bar{A} \cos \delta + \bar{B}(\sin \zeta \cos \delta - \cos \zeta \sin \delta)$
$+ \bar{C}(\cos \zeta \cos \delta + \sin \zeta \sin \delta)$
$+ \bar{D}(\sin 2\zeta \cos \delta - \cos 2\zeta \sin \delta)$
$+ \bar{E}(\cos 2\zeta \cos \delta + \sin 2\zeta \sin \delta).$

From (3) and (4), page 18, we can write

Sin $\delta = \bar{A} \cos \delta + B \sin (\zeta - \delta) + \bar{C} \cos (\zeta - \delta) + \bar{D} \sin (2\zeta - \delta)$
$+ \bar{E} \cos (2\zeta - \delta).$

But $(\zeta - \delta) = \zeta'$, also $(2\zeta - \delta) = (\zeta' + \zeta)$ and $\zeta = (\zeta' + \delta).$
by substitution $\quad \therefore \ (2\zeta - \delta) = (2\zeta' + \delta).$

Hence $\quad \sin \delta = \bar{A} \cos \delta + \bar{B} \sin \zeta' + \bar{C} \cos \zeta' + \bar{D} \sin (2\zeta' + \delta)$
$+ \bar{E} \cos (2\zeta' + \delta) \qquad (11)$

Equation 11 gives a relation between the exact coefficients and the deviation on any compass course (ζ'), but it does not give the deviation explicitly in terms of the compass course and the exact coefficients.

The deviation term (δ) appears on both sides of the equation, and no mathematical process will remove it from the right-hand side. Thus it is not possible to derive an equation giving the deviation explicitly in terms of the compass course and the exact coefficients. We must therefore find by some other means an expression which will give us the deviation in terms of the compass course.

We require an expression similar to the following:

$$\sin \delta = A + B \sin \zeta' + C \cos \zeta' + D \sin 2\zeta' + E \cos 2\zeta' + F \sin 3\zeta'$$
$$+ G \cos 3\zeta' + H \sin 4\zeta', \text{ etc.} \qquad (12)$$

Where A, B, C, etc., are a type of coefficient at the moment undefined and in which the accuracy of the expression will be greater the larger the number of terms used.

Such an expression can be obtained from equation 11 by successive approximation if we first rewrite some of the terms in a different form. Referring then to equation 11:

$$\bar{D} \sin (2\zeta' + \delta) = \bar{D}(\sin 2\zeta' \cos \delta + \cos 2\zeta' \sin \delta)$$
$$= \bar{D} \sin 2\zeta' \cos \delta + \bar{D} \cos 2\zeta' \sin \delta$$

(see (1), p. 18)

$$\bar{E} \cos (2\zeta' + \delta) = \bar{E}(\cos 2\zeta' \cos \delta - \sin 2\zeta' \sin \delta)$$
$$= \bar{E} \cos 2\zeta' \cos \delta - \bar{E} \sin 2\zeta' \sin \delta$$

(see (2), p. 18)

Equation 11 can now be written as follows:

$$\sin \delta = \bar{A} \cos \delta + \bar{B} \sin \zeta' + \bar{C} \cos \zeta' + \bar{D} \sin 2\zeta' \cos \delta$$
$$+ \bar{D} \cos 2\zeta' \sin \delta + \bar{E} \cos 2\zeta' \cos \delta - \bar{E} \sin 2\zeta' \sin \delta \qquad (13)$$

If the compass is well placed we may consider that $\bar{B}$, $\bar{C}$ and $\bar{D}$ are small quantities of the first order and that $\bar{A}$ and $\bar{E}$ are small quantities of the second order. By this is meant simply that $\bar{A}$ or $\bar{E}$ are of the order of the squares of $\bar{B}$, $\bar{C}$ or $\bar{D}$, and if the values of these latter are small, i.e., decimal quantities their squares will be smaller quantities still. Consider, for instance, the quantity 0·3, its square is 0·09, a very much smaller quantity. The actual values of the coefficients are of the order of the sine of the deviation which they cause. They must therefore have values less than unity, and if the deviations are reasonably small (say less than 15°), the assumption made will be sufficiently correct for our purpose. The deviations of the uncorrected well-placed compass in a ship are usually found to be within these limits.

If the deviation is small, then $\sin \delta = \delta$ where δ is circular measure in radians.

Also, if the deviation is small, then $\sin \delta$ is very nearly zero, and $\cos \delta$ is very nearly unity.

Therefore in our first approximation, in which we deal only with quantities of the first order, from equation 13 we can say $\bar{D} \sin 2\zeta' \cos \delta = \bar{D} \sin 2\zeta'$ and $\bar{D} \cos 2\zeta' \sin \delta = 0$, remembering in both cases that $\sin 2\zeta'$ and $\cos 2\zeta'$ are decimal quantities.

The deviation expressed in quantities of the first order (δ') can then be written $\delta' = \bar{B} \sin \zeta' + \bar{C} \cos \zeta' + \bar{D} \sin 2\zeta'$ (from equation 13).

The deviation expressed in quantities of the second order (δ''), for a second approximation, is arrived at in a similar manner, but the degree of accuracy is greater, and though we can assume that

$$\bar{A} \cos \delta = \bar{A}$$

and

$$\bar{E} \cos 2\zeta' \cos \delta = \bar{E} \cos 2\zeta'$$

also

$$\bar{E} \sin 2\zeta' \sin \delta = 0$$

we cannot now neglect the term in the first order approximation $\bar{D} \cos 2\zeta' \sin \delta'$.

The deviation to a second order accuracy is the deviation to the first order accuracy plus the remaining terms and is written

$$\delta'' = \bar{A} + \bar{B} \sin \zeta' + \bar{C} \cos \zeta' + \bar{D} \sin 2\zeta' + \bar{D} \cos 2\zeta' . \delta' + \bar{E} \cos 2\zeta'.$$

The term $\bar{D} \cos 2\zeta' . \delta'$ needs expanding. We know that

$$\delta' = \bar{B} \sin \zeta' + \bar{C} \cos \zeta' + \bar{D} \sin 2\zeta',$$

so we can write

$$\bar{D} \cos 2\zeta' . \delta' = \bar{D} \cos 2\zeta' (\bar{B} \sin \zeta' + \bar{C} \cos \zeta' + \bar{D} \sin 2\zeta')$$
$$= \bar{D}\bar{B} \cos 2\zeta' \sin \zeta' + \bar{D}\bar{C} \cos 2\zeta' \cos \zeta' + \bar{D}^2 \cos 2\zeta' \sin 2\zeta'.$$

Dividing each term by two and multiplying by two we do not alter the values but we get

$$\bar{D} \cos 2\zeta' . \delta' = \frac{\bar{D}\bar{B}}{2} 2 \cos 2\zeta' \sin \zeta' + \frac{\bar{D}\bar{C}}{2} 2 \cos 2\zeta' \cos \zeta'$$
$$+ \frac{\bar{D}^2}{2} 2 \cos 2\zeta' \sin 2\zeta$$

Now $\qquad 2\cos 2\zeta' \sin \zeta' = \sin 3\zeta' - \sin \zeta'$ (see (6) p. 18)

and $\qquad 2\cos 2\zeta' \cos \zeta' = \cos 3\zeta' + \cos \zeta'$ (see (7) p. 18)

also $\qquad 2\cos 2\zeta' \sin 2\zeta' = \sin 4\zeta'$ (see (6) p. 18)

Hence $\bar{D}\cos 2\zeta' \cdot \delta' = \dfrac{\overline{DB}}{2}\sin 3\zeta' - \dfrac{\overline{DB}}{2}\sin \zeta' + \dfrac{\overline{DC}}{2}\cos 3\zeta'$

$$+ \dfrac{\overline{DC}}{2}\cos \zeta' + \dfrac{\bar{D}^2}{2}\sin 4\zeta'.$$

We can now rewrite the equation for the deviation to a second order accuracy

$$\delta'' = \bar{A} + \bar{B}\sin \zeta' + \bar{C}\cos \zeta' + \bar{D}\sin 2\zeta' + \frac{\overline{DB}}{2}\sin 3\zeta' - \frac{\overline{DB}}{2}\sin \zeta'$$

$$+ \frac{\overline{DC}}{2}\cos 3\zeta' + \frac{\overline{DC}}{2}\cos \zeta' + \frac{\bar{D}^2}{2}\sin 4\zeta' + \bar{E}\cos 2\zeta'.$$

Collecting the terms and rearranging we get

$$\delta'' = \bar{A} + \left(\bar{B} - \frac{\overline{DB}}{2}\right)\sin \zeta' + \left(\bar{C} + \frac{\overline{DC}}{2}\right)\cos \zeta' + \bar{D}\sin 2\zeta'$$

$$+ \bar{E}\cos 2\zeta' + \frac{\overline{DB}}{2}\sin 3\zeta' + \frac{\overline{DC}}{2}\cos 3\zeta' + \frac{\bar{D}^2}{2}\sin 4\zeta' \qquad (14)$$

Equation 14 gives an approximate expression for deviation explicity in terms of the exact coefficients and the Compass Course. (Note the deviation term has disappeared from the right-hand side.)

Compare equation 14 with the hypothetical equation 12. It will be seen that they both contain similar terms, so that we can say

$$A = \bar{A}$$

$$B = \bar{B} - \frac{\overline{DB}}{2} \qquad \text{or} \qquad \bar{B} = B + \frac{DB}{2}$$

$$C = \bar{C} + \frac{\overline{DC}}{2} \qquad \text{or} \qquad \bar{C} = C - \frac{DC}{2}$$

$$D = \bar{D}$$

$$E = \bar{E}$$

$$F = \frac{\overline{BD}}{2} \qquad\qquad\qquad = \frac{BD}{2}$$

$$G = \frac{\overline{CD}}{2} \qquad\qquad\qquad = \frac{CD}{2}$$

$$H = \frac{\bar{D}^2}{2} = \frac{D^2}{2}.$$

The terms in equation 12 are called the *Approximate Coefficients*. The relationships between the exact and the approximate coefficients are given above. *F* and *G* are coefficients of sextantal deviation, that is they vary as sin $3\zeta'$ and cos $3\zeta'$ respectively. *F* will have a maximum value on 30°, 90°, 150°, etc., and a minimum value (zero), and will change its sign when passing 0°, 60°, 120°, etc. *G* will have a maximum value on 0°, 60°, 120°, etc., and will have a minimum value (zero), and change its sign when passing 30°, 90°, 150°, etc. *H* is a coefficient of octantal deviation: it varies as sin $4\zeta'$. It will have a maximum value on odd points of the compass, *i.e.*, N. × E., NE. × N., etc., and will have a minimum value (zero) on the even points, *i.e.*, N., NNE., NE., etc., and change its sign on passing these points.

The relationships only hold good if the fundamental equations are valid, that is, if the coefficients are caused by the real magnetic fields of the ship whether of a permanent nature (including sub-permanent) or of an induced nature. Under certain conditions an analysis of deviations may give apparent coefficients. An apparent *A* and/or *E* may be caused by Gaussin Error (p. 117), an unsatisfactory arrangement of the needle system may cause additional sextantal error.

In actual practice the deviations of the uncompensated compass are sufficiently small, so that sextantal and higher order deviations are negligible, and if only the first five terms of equation 12 are used we get

$$\delta = A + B \sin \zeta' + C \cos \zeta' + D \sin 2\zeta' + E \cos 2\zeta' \qquad (15)$$

which is the expression for deviation in most general use.

δ is, of course, the deviation in circular measure, which for small angles is a close approximation to the Natural Sine, so that if sin δ is substituted for δ, the usual Trigonometrical Tables may be used for any calculations required to be made.

Equation 15 may therefore be written

$$\text{Sin } \delta = A + B \sin \zeta' + C \cos \zeta' + D \sin 2\zeta' + E \cos 2\zeta'.$$

If in the equation we put *A*, *C*, *D* and *E* equal to zero, we get

$$\sin \delta = B \sin \zeta'$$

and if $\qquad \zeta' = 90°$ (*i.e.*, East by Compass),

then $$B = \sin \delta$$
or if $$\zeta' = 270° \ (i.e., \text{West by Compass}),$$
then $$B = -\sin \delta.$$

Again, if A, B, D and E are put equal to zero, then we get

$$\sin \delta = C \cos \zeta'$$

and if $$\zeta' = 0° \ (i.e., \text{North by Compass}),$$
then $$C = \sin \delta$$
or if $$\zeta' = 180° \ (i.e., \text{South by Compass}),$$
then $$C = -\sin \delta.$$

Or if A, B, C and E are put equal to zero,

then $$\sin \delta = D \sin 2\zeta'$$
and if $$\zeta' = 45° \ (i.e., \text{NE. by Compass}),$$
then $$D = \sin \delta$$
or if $$\zeta' = 135° \ (i.e., \text{SE. by Compass}),$$
then $$D = -\sin \delta.$$

The same reasoning applies to all the coefficients, and we can state:

The value of a coefficient is the value of the sine of the maximum deviation it can cause.

The sign of a coefficient is dependent on the sign of the deviation it causes in its own positive quadrants, easterly deviation being considered positive and westerly negative.

B varies as $\sin \zeta'$, the positive quadrants for the Sine are the first and second, i.e., between 0° and 180°. B is therefore positive if it causes Easterly deviation on Easterly courses.

C varies as $\cos \zeta'$, the positive quadrants for the Cosine are first and fourth, i.e., between 270° and 90° through North. C is therefore positive if it causes Easterly deviation on Northerly courses.

In dealing with quadrantal deviation as the course is doubled (D varies as $\sin 2\zeta'$ and E varies as $\cos 2\zeta'$), the quadrants must in a sense be halved. The first quadrant is thus from 0° to 45°, the second from 45° to 90°, the third from 90° to 135°, and the fourth from 135° to 180°. From here we can either start again or continue (see Chapter III, p. 16). Thus from 180° to 225° is considered the fifth (or first) quadrant from 225° to 270° the sixth (or second) quadrant, from 270° to 315° the seventh (or third) quadrant, and from 315° to 360° the eighth (or fourth) quadrant.

D is therefore positive if it causes Easterly deviation in the first and second quadrants (or the fifth or sixth), that is between North and East or between South and West by compass respectively.

E by the same reasoning is positive if it causes Easterly deviation in the first and fourth quadrants (or the fifth or eighth), that is between NW. and NE. through North and SE. and SW. through South all by compass respectively.

A is, of course, a coefficient of constant deviation and takes its sign from that of the deviation it causes.

The signs of the sextantal and octantal coefficients can be obtained by similar reasoning. Their quadrants were discussed briefly on p. 83.

For small angles the sine may be considered approximately proportional to the angle, so that if the deviations are small, equation 15 may be written

$$\delta° = A° + B° \sin \zeta' + C° \cos \zeta' + D° \sin 2\zeta' + E° \cos 2\zeta'.$$

CHAPTER XIV

HEELING ERROR (INCLUDING PITCHING ERROR)

WHEN the ship heels the constants or components of her magnetism will, in general, have different values in the heeled position than they have when she is upright.

Suppose the ship is heeled through an angle of $i°$ to starboard, the fundamental equations (see p. 67) may then be written

$$X_i' = X + a_i X + b_i Y + c_i Z + P_i$$
$$Y_i' = Y + d_i X + e_i Y + f_i Z + Q_i$$
$$Z_i' = Z + g_i X + h_i Y + k_i Z + R_i.$$

Consider the components of the ship's permanent magnetism. Force P, acting in the fore and aft line through the compass position, obviously will not change its position or direction with reference to the compass when the ship heels.

$$\therefore P_i = P.$$

Force Q when the ship heels is no longer horizontal (*Fig.* 37).

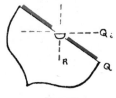

FIG. 37

It must therefore be given a horizontal and vertical component, in effect a new Q and R (see dotted lines). Q_i (the new Q) decreases as the heel increases, becoming zero when the angle of heel is 90°. It will therefore vary as cos i.

$$\therefore Q_i = Q \cos i.$$

The new R will increase as the angle of heel increases, so that the new $R = Q \sin i$.

But we must take into account the effect on the original R. It will be no longer vertical, and must be given vertical and horizontal components, *i.e.*, a new R and a Q (see *Fig.* 38).

86

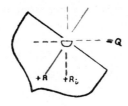

Fig. 38

R_i (the new R) will decrease as the angle of heel increases,

$$\therefore R_i = R \cos i.$$

The new Q, which is negative for a $+R$ as its blue pole moves out to port, will increase with increase of heel,

the new $-Q = R \sin i$

and $Q = -R \sin i.$

Thus when the ship is heeled to starboard,

the effective $Q = Q_i = Q \cos i - R \sin i$

and the effective $R = R_i = Q \sin i + R \cos i.$

The relationship between the constants a_i, b_i, c_i, etc., and a, b, c, etc., that is, the effect of the nine rods when the ship is heeled, is more complicated. The effect is twofold. In general the direction of the rods referred to the earth's magnetic field is altered; so is the direction of the near end of the rods when referred to the compass position.

a Rod. The a rod, as in the case of P, will not alter its position either with reference to the earth's field or with reference to the compass position when the ship heels

$$\therefore a_i = a.$$

b Rod (*Fig. 39*).

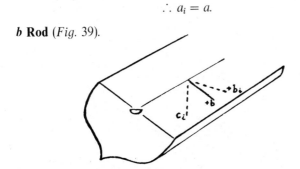

Fig. 39

The original b rod will have two components, a $+b_i$ rod and a $+c_i$ rod. The strength in the b_i rod, due to changing direction with reference to the earth's field, will decrease with increase of heel and vary as cos i, but the near end does not alter its position with reference to the compass position.

Hence $$b_i = b \cos i.$$

The c rod will increase in strength due to changing direction with reference to the earth's field as the ship heels, but the near end will not alter with reference to the compass position

$$\therefore c_i = b \sin i.$$

c **Rod** (*Fig.* 40)

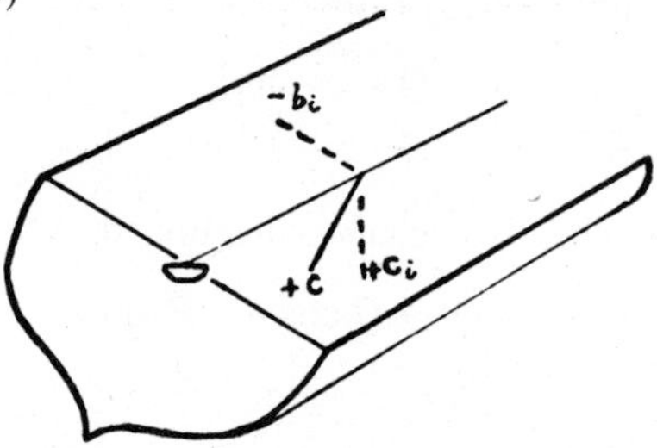

FIG. 40

The original c rod will have two components, a $+c_i$ rod and a $-b_i$ rod. The strength in the c_i rod due to changing direction with reference to the earth's field will decrease as the ship heels, but the near end does not alter with reference to the compass position

$$\therefore c_i = c \cos i.$$

The $-b_i$ rod will increase in strength as the ship heels, but its near end does not alter with reference to the compass position, so that

$$-b_i = c \sin i$$
$$\therefore \quad b_i = -c \sin i.$$

d **Rod** (*Fig.* 41)

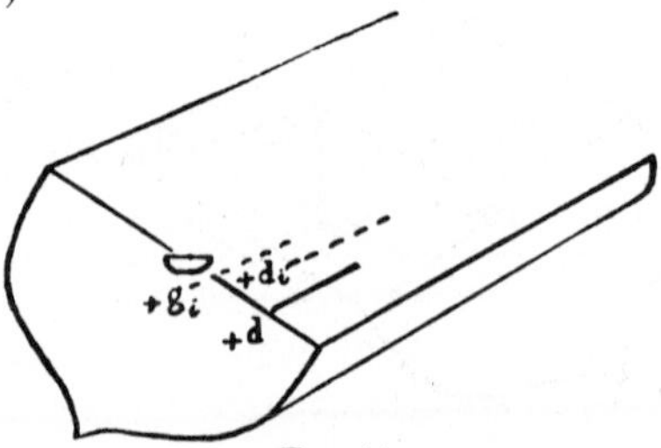

FIG. 41

The d rod will remain fore and aft and horizontal while the ship heels, but its near end, though remaining starboard, will go below the compass position necessitating two components, a $+d_i$ rod and a $+g_i$ rod. (The near end of the g_i rod is, of course, immediately below the compass.) The d_i rod will not change its direction with reference to the earth's field, but its effect will decrease with increase of heel due to its changing position with reference to the compass position

$$\therefore d_i = d \cos i.$$

The g_i rod will not change its direction with reference to the earth's field, but its effect will increase with increase of heel due to its changing position with reference to the compass position.

$$\therefore g_i = d \sin i.$$

e **Rod** (*Figs.* 42, 43 and 44).

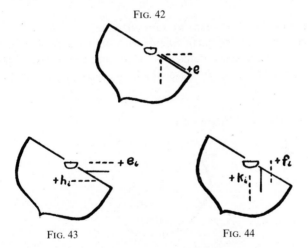

FIG. 42

FIG. 43   FIG. 44

The e rod has not only moved out of the horizontal, but its near end has moved out of the horizontal plane through the compass position. We first of all give it a horizontal and a vertical component (*Fig.* 42), and then deal with each of these separately.

The horizontal component, by reason of its position with reference to the compass, requires two components, a $+e_i$ rod and a $+h_i$ rod (*Fig.* 43).

The e_i rod will decrease in strength, due to changing direction with reference to the earth's field, with increase in heel, and from this cause will vary as $\cos i$, but its effect will also decrease due to change of position with reference to the compass again varying as cos i.

$$\therefore e_i = e \cos i \times \cos i = e \cos^2 i.$$

The h rod will decrease in strength, due to change of direction with reference to the earth's field, with increase of heel, but will increase in effect due to change of position with reference to the compass. The first part varies as cos i and the second as sin i.

$$\therefore h_i = e \cos i \sin i.$$

The vertical component (*Fig.* 44), by reason of its position, also requires two components, a $+f_i$ rod and a $+k_i$ rod.

The f_i rod will increase in strength, due to change of direction with reference to the earth's field, with increase of heel, and vary as sin i, but its effect will decrease due to change of position with reference to the compass and vary as cos i.

$$\therefore f_i = e \sin i \cos i.$$

The k_i rod will increase in strength, due to change of direction with reference to the earth's field, with increase of heel, and vary as sin i, and will also increase in effect due to change of position with reference to the compass which will also vary as sin i.

$$k_i = e \sin^2 i.$$

f **Rod** (*Figs.* 45, 46 and 47).

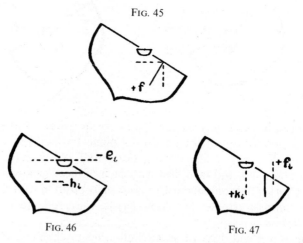

FIG. 45

FIG. 46   FIG. 47

The f rod has not only moved out of the vertical, but its near end has moved below the horizontal plane through the compass. As in the case of the e rod, we first of all give it a horizontal and a vertical component (*Fig.* 45) and then deal with each separately.

The horizontal component (*Fig.* 46) requires two components, a $-e_i$ rod and a $-h_i$ rod.

The e rod will increase in strength, due to change of direction with reference to the earth's field, with increase of heel, and vary as sin i, but its effect will decrease due to change of position with reference to the compass and vary as cos i.

So that
$$-e_i = f \sin i \cos i$$
$$\therefore \quad e_i = -f \sin i \cos i.$$

The h_i rod will increase in strength, due to change of direction with reference to the earth's field, with increase of heel, and will vary as sin i. Its effect due to change of position with reference to the compass, will also increase, and so vary as sin i.

Hence
$$-h_i = f \sin^2 i$$
$$h_i = -f \sin^2 i.$$

The vertical component (*Fig.* 47) requires two components, a $+f_i$ rod and a $+k_i$ rod.

The f_i rod will decrease in strength, due to change of direction with reference to the earth's field, as the ship heels, and vary as cos i, and its effect will also decrease due to change of position with reference to the compass, and vary as cos i.

$$\therefore f_i = f \cos^2 i.$$

The k_i rod will decrease in strength, due to change in direction with reference to the earth's field, as the ship heels, and vary as cos i, but its effect will increase due to change of position with reference to the compass and vary as sin i.

$$\therefore k_i = f \cos i \sin i.$$

g **Rod** (*Figs.* 48 and 49).

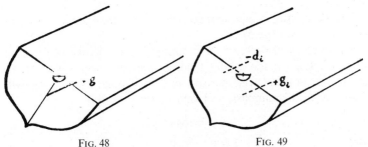

FIG. 48   FIG. 49

When the ship heels to starboard the g rod below the compass moves out to port (*Fig.* 48); it will require two components, a $+g_i$ rod and a $-d_i$ rod (*Fig.* 49).

The g_i rod will not alter its direction with reference to the earth's field, but its effect will decrease with increase of heel due to change of position with reference to the compass, and vary as $\cos i$.

$$\therefore \; g_i = g \cos i.$$

The d_i rod will not alter its direction with reference to the earth's field with increase of heel, but its effect will increase due to change of position with reference to the compass and vary as $\sin i$.

$$\therefore \; -d_i = g \sin i$$

and $$d_i = -g \sin i.$$

h Rod (*Figs.* 50, 51 and 52).

Fig. 50

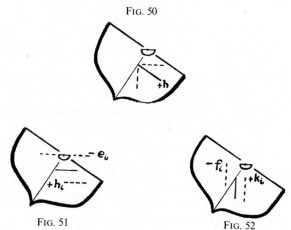

Fig. 51   Fig. 52

The h rod moves out of the horizontal when the ship is inclined, and therefore must have a horizontal and a vertical component (*Fig.* 50).

The horizontal component requires two components, a $-e_i$ rod and a $+h_i$ rod (*Fig.* 51).

The e_i rod will decrease in strength, due to change of direction with reference to the earth's field, as the ship heels, and vary as $\cos i$, but its effect will increase due to change of position with reference to the compass, and vary as $\sin i$, so that

$$-e_i = h \cos i \sin i$$

and $$e_i = -h \cos i \sin i.$$

The h_i rod will decrease in strength, due to change of direction with reference to the earth's field, with increase of heel and vary as cos i, its effect will also decrease due to change of position with reference to the compass and vary as cos i.

$$\therefore h_i = h \cos^2 i.$$

The vertical component requires two components, a $-f_i$ rod and a $+k_i$ rod (*Fig. 52*).

The f_i rod will increase in strength, due to change of direction with reference to the earth's field, as the vessel heels, and vary as sin i. Its effect will also increase due to change of position with reference to the compass and will vary as sin i.

So that $$-f_i = h \sin^2 i$$
$$\therefore \quad f_i = -h \sin^2 i.$$

The k_i rod will increase in strength, due to change of direction with reference to the earth's field, with increase of heel, and vary as sin i, but its effect will decrease due to change of position with reference to the compass and vary as cos i.

$$\therefore k_i = h \sin i \cos i.$$

k Rod (*Figs. 53, 54 and 55*).

FIG. 53

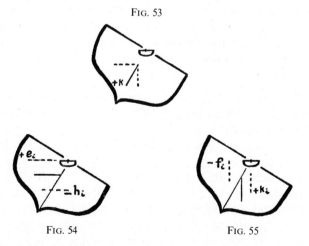

FIG. 54   FIG. 55

The k rod, having moved out of the vertical, will have a horizontal and a vertical component (*Fig. 53*).

The horizontal component will have two components, a $+e_i$ rod and a $-h_i$ rod (*Fig. 54*).

The e_i rod will increase in strength, due to change of direction with reference to the earth's field, with increase of heel, and vary as sin i. Its effect will also increase due to change of position with reference to the compass and vary as sin i.

$$\therefore \ e_i = k \sin^2 i.$$

The h_i rod will increase in strength, due to change of direction with reference to the earth's field, with increase of heel, and vary as sin i, but its effect will decrease due to change of position with reference to the compass and vary as cos i.

$$\therefore \ -h_i = k \sin i \cos i$$

and
$$h_i = -k \sin i \cos i.$$

The vertical component will have two components, a $-f_i$ rod and a $+k_i$ rod (*Fig. 55*).

The f_i rod will decrease in strength, due to change of direction with reference to the earth's field, with increase of heel, and vary as cos i, but its effect will increase due to change of position with reference to the compass and vary as sin i.

$$\therefore \ -f_i = k \cos i \sin i$$

or
$$f_i = -k \cos i \sin i.$$

The k_i rod will decrease in strength, due to change in direction with reference to the earth's field, as the ship heels, and vary as cos i. Its effect will also decrease due to change of position with reference to the compass and vary as cos i.

$$\therefore \ k_i = k \cos^2 i.$$

It will be seen that the above results are all interrelated as in the case of Q and R with the ship heeled. They can best be collected and shown in tabular form.

Table 1 following gives the results obtained above. In the vertical columns under a_i, b_i, $c_i \dots k_i$, are two results given against the applicable horizontal columns headed a, b, $c \dots k$. The first result is the effect due to change of direction of the rod with respect to the earth's field, *i.e.*, the first of the two results obtained in each case above. The second result is the effect due to the change of the near end of the rod with respect to the compass position, *i.e.*, the last of the two results obtained in each case above. The product of each pair of tabulated results will give the final result given in each case above. Where the change is nil a 1 is inserted. For instance, under a_i and opposite a we find 1, 1, and therefore $a_i = a \times 1 \times 1 = a$,

TABLE I

	a_i	b_i	c_i	d_i	e_i	f_i	g_i	h_i	k_i
a	$+1 \quad +1$								
b		$+\cos i \quad +1$	$+\sin i \quad +1$						
c		$-\sin i \quad +1$	$+\cos i \quad +1$						
d				$+1 \quad +\cos i$			$+1 \quad +\sin i$		
e					$+\cos i +\cos i$	$+\sin i +\cos i$		$+\cos i +\sin i$	$+\sin i +\sin i$
f					$-\sin i +\cos i$	$+\cos i +\cos i$		$-\sin i +\sin i$	$+\cos i +\sin i$
g				$+1 \quad -\sin i$			$+1 \quad +\cos i$		
h					$+\cos i -\sin i$	$+\sin i -\sin i$		$+\cos i +\cos i$	$+\sin i +\cos i$
k					$+\sin i +\sin i$	$+\cos i +\sin i$		$-\sin i +\cos i$	$+\cos i +\cos i$

TABLE II

	a_i	b_i	c_i	d_i	e_i	f_i	g_i	h_i	k_i
a	$+1 \quad +1$								
c		$-i \quad +1$	$+1 \quad +1$						
e					$+1 \quad +1$	$+i \quad +1$		$+1 \quad +i$	
g				$+1 \quad -i$			$+1 \quad +1$		
k						$+1 \quad -i$		$-i \quad +1$	$+1 \quad +1$

hence $a_i = a$ the first result obtained. Again, under k_i and opposite k, we find $+\cos i$, $+\cos i$, and so that part of $k_i = k \times \cos i \times \cos i$, whence $k_i = k \cos^2 i$, the last result obtained above.

To obtain the complete value, all the results under each heading must be added together, for instance, from the Table

$$k_i = e \sin^2 i + f \cos i \sin i + h \sin i \cos i + k \cos^2 i$$

or again

$$e = e_i \cos^2 i + f_i \sin i \cos i + h_i \cos i \sin i + k_i \sin^2 i.$$

These latter expressions should be checked with the results obtained in the above investigations.

To obtain an expression for Heeling Error from the values of P, Q and R in the heeled condition together with the data given in Table I for the rods would be a complicated and laborious process.

If the compass is assumed to be placed, as it usually is, so that the soft iron is symmetrically arranged about its position, then the values of b, d, f, h, $\overline{A}$ and $\overline{E}$ will all be zero. Also, if the angle of heel is considered small enough so that $\sin i = i$ (circular measure), and $\cos i = 1$, also that $i^2 = 0$ (the square of a small decimal quantity may, in an approximation, be considered negligible), then referring to Table I and omitting the values against b, d, f and h (left-hand headings) we get

$$a_i = a,\ b_i = -ic,\ c_i = c,\ d_i = -ig,$$

$$e_i = e \text{ (for } \sin i \times \sin i = i \times i = i^2 = 0 \text{ by assumption),}$$

$$f_i = i(e - k),\ g_i = g,\ h_i = i(e - k),\ k_i = k.$$

These relationships are shown in tabular form in Table II, which should be compared with Table I, using the aforementioned assumptions. It should be noted that though b, d, f and h are all assumed to be zero, b_i, d_i, f_i and h_i still appear.

Using these assumptions, we can obtain expressions for the coefficients when the ship is heeled, using Tables I or II. Table II is all that is needed, but the process may be more easily understood if some reference is made to Table I.

Coefficient λ_i

$\lambda = 1 + \dfrac{a + e}{2}$. From Table II, $a = a_i$ and $e = e_i$, the remaining factors given for e do not apply as they affect only the applicable coefficients.

We now require a_i and e_i in terms of the actual rods, and in Table II under a_i we see that $a_i = a$ and under e_i we see that $e_i = e$. Therefore we can say that $\lambda_i = 1 + \dfrac{a+e}{2}$

$$\therefore \lambda_i = \lambda.$$

Coefficient $\bar{A}_i$

$\bar{A} = \dfrac{d-b}{2\lambda}$. From Table I, $d = d_i$ (remembering our assumptions, and that the remaining factors are not applicable). Similarly $b = b_i$. From Table I again, reading vertically, we get:

$$d_i = d - ig \text{ and } b_i = b - ic$$

$$\therefore \bar{A}_i = \frac{(d-ig)-(b-ic)}{2\lambda} = \frac{d-ig-b+ic}{2\lambda}$$

$$= \frac{d-b}{2\lambda} + \frac{i(c-g)}{2\lambda} = \bar{A} + \frac{i(c-g)}{2\lambda}$$

But $\bar{A} = 0$ by assumption,

$$\therefore \bar{A}_i = \frac{i(c-g)}{2\lambda} \text{ which is the result which we should have obtained}$$

if Table II had been used.

Coefficient $\bar{B}_i$

$\bar{B} = \dfrac{1}{\lambda}\left(c \tan \theta + \dfrac{P}{H}\right)$. It has already been shown that $P_i = P$. From Table II, $c = c_i$ (neglecting b_i as inapplicable), and $c_i = c$

$$\bar{B}_i = \bar{B}.$$

Coefficient $\bar{C}_i$

$\bar{C} = \dfrac{1}{\lambda}\left(f \tan \theta + \dfrac{Q}{H}\right)$. We have seen that

$$Q_i = Q \cos i - R \sin i$$
$$= Q - iR \qquad \text{(approximately)}.$$

The appropriate part of f from Table I $= f_i$

and

$$f_i = ie + f - ik \qquad (h = 0)$$
$$= f + i(e-k).$$

Then
$$\bar{C}_i = \frac{1}{\lambda}\left[\left\{f + i(e - k)\right\}\tan\theta + \frac{Q - iR}{H}\right]$$

$$= \frac{1}{\lambda}\left(f\tan\theta + \frac{Q}{H}\right) + \frac{1}{\lambda}\left[i(e - k)\tan\theta - i\frac{R}{H}\right]$$

$$\therefore \bar{C}_i = \bar{C} + \frac{i}{\lambda}\left[(e - k)\tan\theta - \frac{R}{H}\right].$$

Coefficient $\bar{D}_i$

$$\bar{D} = \frac{a - e}{2\lambda}.$$

From Table II $a = a_i$ and $a_i = a$ and $e = e_i$ and $e_i = e$.

Hence
$$\bar{D}_i = \frac{a - e}{2\lambda} \quad \text{and} \quad \bar{D}_i = \bar{D}.$$

Coefficient $\bar{E}_i$

$$\bar{E} = \frac{d + b}{2\lambda}.$$

From Table I $d = d_i$ and $b = b_i$.
From Table II $d_i = -ig$ and $b_i = -ic$.

Therefore
$$\bar{E}_i = \frac{-ig - ic}{2\lambda} = \frac{-i(c + g)}{2\lambda}.$$

The deviation in terms of the exact coefficients and the Compass Course when the ship is heeled can thus be written

$$\text{Sin } \delta_i = \bar{A}_i\cos\delta_i + \bar{B}_i\sin\zeta' + \bar{C}_i\cos\zeta' + \bar{D}_i\sin(2\zeta' + \delta_i)$$
$$+ \bar{E}_i\cos(2\zeta' + \delta_i) \tag{11a}$$

The Heeling Error on any ship's heading by compass is the difference between the deviation when the ship is heeled and the deviation when the ship is upright.

As $\sin\delta_i$ and $\sin\delta$ may be considered small, the heeling error may be written $(\delta_i - \delta)$. It is equal to equation 11a (above), minus equation 11 (page 79), the mathematics of which is given in full at the end of the chapter and from which it will be seen that

$$(\delta_i - \delta) = \frac{i}{\lambda}\left[(e - k)\tan\theta - \frac{R}{H}\right]\cos\zeta' + i\frac{c}{\lambda}\sin^2\zeta' - i\frac{g}{\lambda}\cos^2\zeta'.$$

This is the Heeling Error Expression. The semi-circular part, *i.e.*,

$$\frac{i}{\lambda}\left[(e-k)\tan\theta - \frac{R}{H}\right]\cos\zeta'$$

is all that in practice need be considered.

The part of the heeling error due to the *c* rod, *i.e.*, $i\frac{c}{\lambda}\sin^2\zeta'$, is automatically corrected by the Flinders bar, which should always be in place when the heeling error correction is made.

That part due to the *g* rod, *i.e.*, $i\frac{g}{\lambda}\cos^2\zeta'$, is not conducive to mechanical correction, and is a negligible quantity in most ships. Any effect which may be present is best left out of the mechanical correction by having the ship's head in an easterly or westerly direction when compensation for heeling error is made.

Coefficient J

$$\frac{1}{\lambda}\left[(e-k)\tan\theta - \frac{R}{H}\right]$$

is termed the Heeling Error Coefficient *J*.

J is usually negative for compass positions on the upper deck of ships built in the northern hemisphere, and causes a deviation to the high side.

Note. Heeling error to the low side is usually considered positive. It must also be emphasised that a negative *J* (or a positive heeling error) can produce both an easterly and westerly deviation depending on whether the ship is heeled to port or starboard and, of course, on the direction of the ship's head. When making calculations involving heeling error, easterly deviation is still considered positive, and westerly negative. It is advisable also to consider an angle of heel to starboard as $+i°$ and an angle of heel to port as $-i°$.

Referring to the expression, it will be seen that coefficient *J* is due to three effects which may be said to be the three principal causes of heeling error. They are:

1. The effect of the vertical component *R* of the ship's permanent magnetic field. For a compass placed on the upper deck in a ship built in the northern hemisphere, *R* is normally positive. The effect due to *R* varies inversely as *H*.

2. The effect of vertical induction in soft iron beneath the compass of the $+k$ rod type. This varies as the tangent of the Dip.

3. The effect of vertical induction in soft iron of the e rod type which acquires a vertical component when the ship heels. This component also varies as the tangent of the Dip.

All three vary inversely as λ and directly as the cosine of the compass course. They may also be considered as varying directly as the angle of heel. (For small angles of heel we can write $\sin 2i = 2 \sin i$.)

Coefficient μ (Mu)

Fundamental equation 3 (see page 67) gives the total vertical force Z' acting at the compass position in terms of the various components, i.e.,

$$Z' = Z + gX + hY + kZ + R.$$

This can be written (see page 67)

$$Z' = Z + gH \cos \zeta - hH \sin \zeta + kZ + R.$$

Divide by Z and we get

$$\frac{Z'}{Z} = 1 + g \cot \theta \cos \zeta - h \cot \theta \sin \zeta + k + \frac{R}{Z}$$

or

$$\frac{Z'}{Z} = 1 + k + \frac{R}{Z} + \frac{g}{\tan \theta} \cos \zeta - \frac{h}{\tan \theta} \sin \zeta.$$

The mean value of $\dfrac{Z'}{Z}$ for all points of the ship's head in azimuth

is $1 + k + \dfrac{R}{Z} = \mu$ where μ is the ratio of the mean value of the total

vertical force at the compass position to that of the earth's force when the ship is upright.

For the heeling error to be zero,

$$(e - k) \tan \theta - \frac{R}{H} = 0$$

so that

$$(e - k) \tan \theta = \frac{R}{H}$$

and

$$(e - k) = \frac{R}{H} \cot \theta = \frac{R}{H} \times \frac{H}{Z} = \frac{R}{Z}$$

thus
$$e - k = \frac{R}{Z}$$

then
$$e = k + \frac{R}{Z}$$

and
$$1 + e = 1 + k + \frac{R}{Z} = \mu.$$

The heeling error is zero if $\mu = 1 + e$.
Alternatively, since $1 + e = \lambda(1 - \bar{D})$,
the heeling error will be zero if

$$\lambda(1 - \bar{D}) = \mu.$$

For
$$\lambda(1 - \bar{D}) = \lambda\left(1 - \frac{a - e}{2\lambda}\right)$$

$$= \lambda - \frac{a - e}{2}$$

$$= 1 + \frac{a + e}{2} - \frac{a - e}{2}$$

$$= 1 + \frac{a + e - a + e}{2}$$

$$= 1 + \frac{2e}{2}$$

$$= 1 + e.$$

Correction of Heeling Error. This is usually effected with the use of a Vertical Force Instrument.

The Vertical Force Instrument consists of a magnetised needle of symmetrical shape and of homogeneous material, so that its centre of gravity is at its geometrical centre. The needle is pivoted so that it is free to move in a vertical plane, and so that before magnetisation its position of equilibrium is horizontal. It is usually graduated along its length by equally spaced divisions in either direction from its centre, and carries a balancing weight which may be attached to, and adjusted along, either arm.

In northern magnetic latitudes, when placed in the magnetic meridian, the needle will dip with its north end below the horizontal. This may be considered due to the earth's vertical force Z.

If the weight is attached to the upper arm and adjusted so that the needle lies horizontal on its pivot, the earth's vertical force will be neutralised. The moment of the weight about the axis of rotation will be a measure of the earth's vertical force Z.

If the same weight is used for all experiments, its mass may be considered as unity, and Z is proportional to n where n is the distance of the weight from the centre, measured in terms of the number of graduations on the scale. (Always read from the inside edge of the weight.)

If such an experiment is carried out in two different places or positions, then

$$\frac{Z}{Z'} = \frac{n}{n'}$$

where Z and Z' are the vertical forces at the first and second positions respectively, and n and n' the number of divisions the weight is moved out at the first and second positions respectively.

Hence, if the instrument is first levelled at a position where it is under the influence of the earth's force alone, and is then brought to the ship and placed in the compass position and in the magnetic meridian (the compass bowl must be removed for this purpose), one end of the needle will dip below the horizontal due to the ship's vertical force alone. Permanent magnets may then be placed in the heeling-error bucket in the binnacle and adjusted so that the needle again lies horizontal. The ship's vertical force at the compass position will then be neutralised. With the ship upright, however, the e rod part of the heeling error will have no effect on the needle of the Vertical Force Instrument and will not have been compensated for, so that in the condition considered above the ship's vertical force Z' is, in the heeled condition, equal to Z the earth's vertical force plus the e rod effect. Induction in the e rod when inclined is due to Z, hence

$$Z' = Z + eZ$$
$$= Z(1 + e).$$

We have seen that

$$\frac{Z'}{Z} = \frac{n'}{n}$$

$$\therefore \frac{Z(1 + e)}{Z} = \frac{n'}{n} = 1 + e$$

$$\therefore \qquad n' = n(1 + e) = n\mu.$$

Thus if n, the number of divisions required to neutralise the earth's vertical force, is multiplied by μ, the result will be n', and if the weight is adjusted to n' divisions before correcting the heeling error, the e rod effect will be accounted for. When the spheres are in place the value of the e rod is much reduced, and becomes e_2 and then

$$1 + e_2 = \mu_2$$

and the equation for heeling-error correction becomes

$$n' = n\mu_2.$$

μ_2 is termed the Ship's Multiplier.

It will be seen later that μ_2 is numerically equal to λ_2, and it is the value of the latter which is normally found.

As the heeling error is caused partly by permanent magnetism and partly by magnetism induced in soft iron, the correction by means of permanent magnets will not hold good with change of magnetic latitude. If a Vertical Force Instrument is carried on board and the value of n, the number of divisions the weight is required to be moved out to balance the needle where the earth's vertical force Z, is known, then the number of divisions n_2 at which the weight should be set to adjust the heeling error at a place where the earth's vertical force is Z_2 is given by

$$n_2 = n\frac{Z_2}{Z} \times \text{Ship's Multiplier.}$$

If the value of the ship's multiplier is not known, an approximate value of λ_2 based on experience of its value in other similar ships may be used or, alternatively, use

$$n_2 = n\frac{Z_2}{Z}$$

and then in the adjustment leave the north end of the needle just slightly above the horizontal in the northern hemisphere or slightly below in the southern hemisphere. The value of the ship's multiplier should, however, be known.

In the event of no Vertical Force Instrument being available, and the compass becoming unsteady in a seaway due to uncorrected error causing the compass to oscillate as the vessel rolls, then by raising or lowering the heeling-error bucket a position will be found where the compass will become steadier. It is not advisable to experiment in this way with the standard compass, as it will alter the value of Coefficient B, but it is a perfectly seamanlike method of obtaining a steady steering compass.

Harvey-Raynes Heeling Error Corrector. Any alteration in the position of the heeling-error magnets causes a change of induction in the Flinders bar and alters the value of coefficient *B*. This occurring after the compass has been corrected, is a big disadvantage in the normal method of correction. This is especially so due to the fact that the whole of the heeling error is corrected by means of permanent magnets, and therefore can only remain valid in one magnetic latitude. *Figure* 56 shows diagrammatically the forces involved.

The vertical direct force corrects heeling error; the horizontal force from induction in the Flinders bar modifies the value of coefficient *B*. Hence any alteration of the value of the direct force to adjust heeling error automatically alters the value of the induced force,

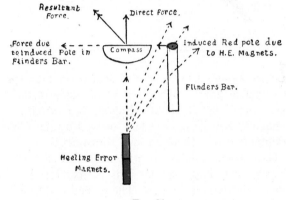

FIG. 56

and consequently coefficient *B* will simultaneously require readjustment.

The resultant of these two forces is in a direction inclined from the vertical and toward the direction of the horizontal force.

If the heeling-error correcting magnets were sloped and placed in the vertical plane defined by the Flinders bar and the compass pivot, an angle could be found at which the direct force from the magnets produced a component horizontal force equal and opposite to that produced by induction in the Flinders bar. Any increase or decrease in the strength of the magnets at this angle would not then produce any horizontal field, as the direct and induced fields would increase or decrease by the same amounts. Thus the strength could be adjusted so that the resultant vertical field would correct the heeling error and, moreover, the adjustment could be made at any time when, due to change of magnetic latitude, the compass had become unsteady. *Figure* 57 (overleaf) illustrates these conditions.

The angle of slope of the heeling-error magnets would depend on the length of Flinders bar, as any variation in length of bar would

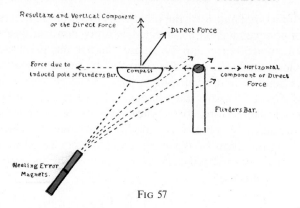

FIG 57

alter the strength of the induced field, all other conditions remaining constant.

The Harvey-Raynes Corrector is designed on these principles. It consists of a magnet carrier fitted on the side of the binnacle diametrically opposite to that of the Flinders bar, in such a position that the magnets will lie in the plane defined by the Flinders bar and the compass pivot. There are two adjustments.

The first is a locked angular adjustment which, being set by means of a scale, fixes the slope so that it is correct for the length of Flinders bar indicated on the scale. The second is a trial and error adjustment in which the number and polarity of the magnets are altered at will, so as to correct (or adjust) the heeling error without any fear of introducing any unknown semicircular deviations. This device is illustrated in *Fig.* 58. Another form consists of a magnet

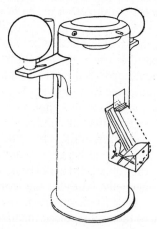

FIG. 58

MATHEMATICS OF THE HEELING ERROR

The deviation when the ship is heeled may be written

$$\delta_i = \cos \delta_i \left[\bar{A} + i\left(\frac{c-g}{2\lambda}\right)\right] + \bar{B} \sin \zeta' + \left[\bar{C} + \frac{i}{\lambda}(e-k)\tan\theta - \frac{i}{\lambda}\frac{R}{H}\right]\cos\zeta' + \bar{D}\sin(2\zeta' + \delta_i) + \left[\bar{E} - i\left(\frac{c+g}{2\lambda}\right)\right]\cos(2\zeta' + \delta_i) \quad (11b)$$

The deviation when the ship is upright may be written

$$\delta = \bar{A}\cos\delta + \bar{B}\sin\zeta' + \bar{C}\cos\zeta' + \bar{D}\sin(2\zeta' + \delta) + \bar{E}\cos(2\zeta' + \delta) \quad (11)$$

Subtracting (11) from (11b) we get $(\delta_i - \delta)$, the heeling error, and removing the brackets the equation becomes

$$(\delta_i - \delta) = \bar{A}\cos\delta_i - \bar{A}\cos\delta + i\left(\frac{c-g}{2\lambda}\right)\cos\delta_i + \bar{B}\sin\zeta' - \bar{B}\sin\zeta' + \bar{C}\cos\zeta' - \bar{C}\cos\zeta' + \frac{i}{\lambda}\left[(e-k)\tan\theta - \frac{R}{H}\right]\cos\zeta'$$

$$+ \bar{D}\sin(2\zeta' + \delta_i) - \bar{D}\sin(2\zeta' + \delta) + \bar{E}\cos(2\zeta' + \delta_i) - \bar{E}\cos(2\zeta' + \delta) - i\left(\frac{c+g}{2\lambda}\right)\cos(2\zeta' + \delta_i).$$

Since we can say $\cos\delta_i = \cos\delta = 1$, and rearranging we get

$$(\delta_i - \delta) = \frac{i}{\lambda}\left[(e-k)\tan\theta - \frac{R}{H}\right]\cos\zeta' + i\left(\frac{c-g}{2\lambda}\right) - i\left(\frac{c+g}{2\lambda}\right)\cos(2\zeta' + \delta_i)$$

$$= \frac{i}{\lambda}\left[(e-k)\tan\theta - \frac{R}{H}\right]\cos\zeta' + \frac{i}{2\lambda}(c - g - c\cos2\zeta' - g\cos2\zeta')\text{*}$$

$$= \frac{i}{\lambda}\left[(e-k)\tan\theta - \frac{R}{H}\right]\cos\zeta' + \frac{i}{2\lambda}\left[c(1 - \cos^2\zeta' + \sin^2\zeta') - g(1 + \cos^2\zeta' - \sin^2\zeta')\right]\dagger$$

$$= \frac{i}{\lambda}\left[(e-k)\tan\theta - \frac{R}{H}\right]\cos\zeta' + \frac{i}{2\lambda}\left[c(1 - 1 + \sin^2\zeta' + \sin^2\zeta') - g(1 + \cos^2\zeta' - 1 + \cos^2\zeta')\right]\ddagger$$

$$= \frac{i}{\lambda}\left[(e-k)\tan\theta - \frac{R}{H}\right]\cos\zeta' + \frac{i}{\lambda}\left(\frac{2c\sin^2\zeta'}{2}\right) - \frac{i}{\lambda}\left(\frac{2g\cos^2\zeta'}{2}\right)$$

$$= \frac{i}{\lambda}\left[(e-k)\tan\theta - \frac{R}{H}\right]\cos\zeta' + \frac{i}{\lambda}c\sin^2\zeta' - \frac{i}{\lambda}g\cos^2\zeta', \text{ which is the heeling-error expression. (See page 98.)}$$

* Since δ_i is considered a very small quantity $(2\zeta' + \delta_i) = 2\zeta'$ approximately.
† See equation (10), page 18.
‡ $\cos^2\zeta' = 1 - \sin^2\zeta'$, see page 18, thus $1 - \cos^2\zeta' = 1 - 1 + \sin^2\zeta'$, similarly $-\sin^2\zeta' = -1 + \cos^2\zeta'$.

carrier inside the binnacle in which the angle does not change but the whole carrier slides sideways, toward or away from the Flinders bar, so that it may be adjusted to the correct position for the length of Flinders bar required. A setting dial is fitted on which the lengths of Flinders bar are marked.

The Harvey-Raynes type of heeling-error corrector has been adopted by the Royal Navy. Merchant Ships trading from high North latitudes to high South latitudes and *vice versa* would benefit by fitting the Harvey-Raynes corrector to the Standard Compass.

Pitching Error. So far when dealing with the theory of deviation we have considered right hand rotation only, that is to say right-handed rotation about the keel axis gives the magnetic course and right-handed rotation about the forward axis gives the positive angle of roll, *i.e.* to starboard. For the positive angle of pitch right-handed rotation about the starboard axis is taken, *i.e.* the pitch or change of trim which puts the ship "by the stem".

Suppose the ship to be pitched by the stem through an angle p the fundamental equations can then be written:

$$X_p^1 = X + a_p X + b_p Y + c_p Z + P_p$$
$$Y_p^1 = Y + d_p X + e_p Y + f_p Z + Q_p$$
$$Z_p^1 = Z + g_p X + h_p Y + k_p Z + R_p$$

Now by following exactly the same reasoning as was used in investigating the heeling error we can arrive at the following coefficients:

$$\bar{A}_p = \frac{1}{\lambda} \frac{d_p - b_p}{2} = 0$$

$$\bar{B}_p = \frac{1}{\lambda}\left(c_p \tan\theta + \frac{P_p}{H}\right) = -\frac{p}{\lambda}\left(c_p \tan\theta - \frac{R}{H}\right)$$

$$= -\frac{p}{\lambda}\left\{(e_2 - k)\tan\theta - \frac{R}{H}\right\}$$

$$\bar{C}_p = \frac{1}{\lambda}\left(f_p \tan\theta + \frac{Q_p}{H}\right) = 0$$

$$\bar{D}_p = \frac{1}{\lambda} \frac{a_p - e_p}{2} = \frac{gp}{2\lambda}$$

$$\bar{E}_p = \frac{1}{\lambda} \frac{d_p + b_p}{2} = 0$$

The absence of $\bar{A}_p$ and $\bar{E}_p$ indicates that the symmetry of the arrangement of iron about the plane of X and Z is not upset. Apart from the mathematical proof this must be obvious if a little thought is given to the practical effect of the ship pitching.

Hence in radians

$$\delta_p = \frac{-p}{\lambda} \left\{ (e_2 - k) \tan \theta - \frac{R}{H} \right\} \sin \zeta^1 + \frac{pg}{2\lambda} \sin 2\zeta^1$$

This is the simplified pitching error expression of which in a well placed compass the semi-circular part, i.e.:

$$\frac{-p}{\lambda} \left\{ (e_2 - k) \tan \theta - \frac{R}{H} \right\}$$

is all that in practice need be considered.

This term may be written:

$$(-p)J \sin \zeta^1 \quad \text{where} \quad J = \frac{1}{\lambda} \left\{ (e_2 - k) \tan \theta - \frac{R}{H} \right\}$$

which is exactly the same coefficient as that found for the heeling error (see page 98).

Pitching error varies as $\sin \zeta^1$ and is therefore at a maximum on East and West and zero on North and South headings.

For a symmetrically placed compass the heeling error coefficient and the pitching error coefficient are numerically the same each indicating the number of degrees of error per degree of heel or pitch. Therefore as in the case of heeling error if μ_2 is made equal to λ_2 the pitching error is removed. As previously stated an angle of $1°$ to starboard is considered positive and an angle of $p°$ or pitch or trim by the stem is also considered positive.

CHAPTER XV

ANALYSIS OF DEVIATIONS

In order to compensate for the various magnetic fields at the compass position, it is advisable to know the values of the Approximate Coefficients.

To find their values, the number of observations taken must be at least that of the number of coefficients it is required to find.

For instance, if the coefficients A, B, C, D and E are required, then as there are five unknowns, at least five observations for deviation on different ship's heads must be taken in order to give five equations of the form

$$\delta = A + B \sin \zeta' + C \cos \zeta' + D \sin 2\zeta' + E \cos 2\zeta'.$$

(See page 83.)

The values of the coefficients may then be obtained by the normal process of elimination used in solving simultaneous equations. This is a laborious process, description of which may be found in the *Admiralty Manual of Deviations*, and will not be included here.

If, however, the courses on which the deviations are found are equally spaced round the compass, the method becomes much more simple, as the normal equations reduce to the following simple form for five unknowns:

$$\Sigma \delta = nA$$
$$\Sigma \delta \sin \zeta' = \tfrac{1}{2}nB$$
$$\Sigma \delta \cos \zeta' = \tfrac{1}{2}nC$$
$$\Sigma \delta \sin 2\zeta' = \tfrac{1}{2}nD$$
$$\Sigma \delta \cos 2\zeta' = \tfrac{1}{2}nE$$

where n is the number of observations taken.

The coefficients thus found are the best possible values (based on the least squares principle) that can be obtained from the recorded observations.

The sum of the deviations is therefore equal to n times A.

The sum of the deviations each multiplied by the sine of its respective course is equal to a half n times B, and so on.

107

Observations for deviations on at least eight equidistant points is normally considered the minimum to give accurate results, but sixteen is more satisfactory if there is the possibility of sextantal and/or octantal errors.

The calculations are best made in tabular form, deviations obtained on the even points being used. (See example, page 111a.)

For the full calculation nineteen columns are required.

1. The first column contains the ship's head by compass, *i.e.* N, NNE, NE, etc.

2. The second column contains the number of the point of the compass corresponding to the ship's head, *i.e.*, 0, 2, 4, etc.

3. The third column is headed No. 1, and contains the values of the deviations corresponding to the direction of the ship's head.

4. The next column is headed No. 2, and contains the values of the sines of the corresponding angles of the ship's head reckoned from north.

5. The next column, headed No. 3, contains the products of column No. 1 and column No. 2, that is the deviation times the sine of the compass course.

6. The next column (No. 4) contains the cosines of the corresponding angles of the ship's head reckoned from north.

7. Column 5 contains the products of columns No. 1 and No. 4, that is, the deviation times the cosine of the compass course.

8. Column 6 contains the values of the sines of twice the compass course measured from north.

9. Column 7 contains the products of columns No. 1 and No. 6, that is, the deviation times the sine of twice the compass course.

10. Column 8 contains the cosines of twice the compass course reckoned from north.

11. Column 9 contains the products of columns No. 1 and No. 8, that is, the deviation times the cosine of twice the compass course.

12. Column 10 contains the sines of three times the compass course reckoned from north.

13. Column 11 contains the products of columns No. 1 and No. 10, that is, the deviation times the sine of three times the compass course.

14. Column 12 contains the cosines of three times the compass course.

15. Column 13 contains the products of columns No. 1 and No. 12.

16. Column 14 contains the sines of four times the compass course reckoned from north.

17. Column 15 contains the products of columns No. 1 and No. 14.

18. Column 16 contains the cosines of four times the compass course reckoned from north.

19. The final column (No. 17) contains the products of columns No. 1 and No. 16.

The algebraic sum of column 1 is equal to nA, where n is the number of observations taken, in this case 16, and A is the Approximate Coefficient. Therefore the algebraic sum divided by n (16) gives the value of coefficient A in terms of the deviation.

The algebraic sum of column 3 is $\dfrac{n}{2} B$, i.e., in this case $8B$, this sum divided by 8 is the value of coefficient B in terms of the maximum deviation caused.

The algebraic sums of columns 5, 7, 9, 11, 13, 15 and 17 are equal to $\dfrac{n}{2} C, \dfrac{n}{2} D, \dfrac{n}{2} E, \dfrac{n}{2} F, \dfrac{n}{2} G, \dfrac{n}{2} H$ and $\dfrac{n}{2} K$ respectively, and if therefore each sum is divided by 8, we get the values of coefficients C, D, E, F, G, H and K in terms of the maximum deviation respectively caused.

Coefficients F and G and H and K are the two sextantal and the two octantal coefficients of deviation respectively. If these coefficients are known to be negligible, calculations need only be carried as far as column headed No. 9.

If one of the sixteen equidistant observations is missing, assume, as a first approximation, that the deviation on the missing ship's head is zero, and calculate coefficients A', B', C', D' and E' in the tabular form described above. Then, with these values, calculate the missing deviation, using equation (15), i.e.,

$$\delta' = A' + B' \sin \zeta' + C' \cos \zeta' + D' \sin 2\zeta' + E' \cos 2\zeta' \quad (15')$$

Using $\dfrac{16}{11}$ of the deviation so found, recalculate the values of coefficients A, B, C, D and E by inserting this value in column No. 1 against the appropriate ship's head.

Proof. Let the missing deviation be Δ on ζ_1' where ζ_1' is any one of the sixteen equidistant points. Let A', B', C', D' and E' be the values of the coefficients calculated on the assumption that the missing deviation is zero.

Then
$$16A = 16A' + \Delta$$
$$8B = 8B' + \Delta \sin \zeta_1'$$

Ē

$$8\,C = 8\,C' + \Delta\cos\zeta'_1$$
$$8\,D = 8\,D' + \Delta\sin 2\zeta'_1$$
$$8\,E = 8\,E' + \Delta\cos 2\zeta'_1$$

whence

$$A + B\sin\zeta'_1 + C\cos\zeta'_1 + D\sin 2\zeta'_1 + E\cos 2\zeta'_1$$

$$= A' + \frac{\Delta}{16} + \left(B' + \frac{\Delta}{8}\sin\zeta'_1\right)\sin\zeta'_1 + \left(C' + \frac{\Delta}{8}\cos\zeta'_1\right)\cos\zeta'_1$$

$$+ \left(D' + \frac{\Delta}{8}\sin 2\zeta'_1\right)\sin 2\zeta'_1 + \left(E' + \frac{\Delta}{8}\cos 2\zeta'_1\right)\cos 2\zeta'_1$$

$$= A' + B'\sin\zeta'_1 + C'\cos\zeta'_1 + D'\sin 2\zeta'_1 + E'\cos 2\zeta'_1 + \frac{\Delta}{16}$$

$$+ \frac{\Delta}{8}\sin^2\zeta'_1 + \frac{\Delta}{8}\cos^2\zeta'_1 + \frac{\Delta}{8}\sin^2 2\zeta'_1 + \frac{\Delta}{8}\cos^2 2\zeta'_1$$

$$= A' + B'\sin\zeta'_1 + C'\cos\zeta'_1 + D'\sin 2\zeta'_1 + E'\cos 2\zeta'_1$$

$$+ \frac{\Delta}{8}(\tfrac{1}{2} + \sin^2\zeta'_1 + \cos^2\zeta'_1 + \sin^2 2\zeta'_1 + \cos^2 2\zeta'_1)$$

$$= A' + B'\sin\zeta'_1 + C'\cos\zeta'_1 + D'\sin 2\zeta'_1 + E'\cos 2\zeta'_1$$

$$+ \frac{\Delta}{8}(\tfrac{1}{2} + 1 + 1)$$

$$= A' + B'\sin\zeta'_1 + C'\cos\zeta'_1 + D'\sin 2\zeta'_1 + E'\cos 2\zeta'_1 + \frac{5}{16}\Delta.$$

Therefore
$$\Delta = \delta' + \frac{5}{16}\Delta$$

where δ' is the approximate missing deviation calculated using A', B', C', D' and E'. (See equation 15'.)

Hence
$$\delta' = \Delta - \frac{5}{16}\Delta = \frac{11}{16}\Delta$$

and
$$\Delta = \frac{16}{11}\delta'.$$

If having calculated the Approximate Coefficients, the values of the Exact Coefficients are required, they may be found by using the expressions found on page 82, *e.g.*,

S.S. *WEATHER RECORDER*
Computed Coefficients from an analysis of deviations as found on 4th January 1949 after vessel was struck by lightning

No. of Points	Ships' head by compass points	1 Dev.	2 $\sin\zeta'$	3 1×2	4 $\cos\zeta'$	5 1×4	6 $\sin2\zeta'$	7 1×6	8 $\cos2\zeta'$	9 1×8	10 $\sin3\zeta'$	11 1×10	12 $\cos3\zeta'$	13 1×12	14 $\sin4\zeta'$	15 1×14	16 $\cos4\zeta'$	17 1×16
0	N	+25·0	0·0	0·0	1·0	+25·0	0·0	0·0	1·0	+25·0	0·0	0·0	1·0	+25·0	0·0	0·0	1·0	+25·0
2	NNE	+31·0	0·383 (S2)	+11·8	0·924 (S6)	+28·6	+0·707 (S4)	+22·0	+0·707 (S4)	22·0	0·924 (S6)	+28·6	0·383 (S2)	+11·8	1·0	+31·0	0·0	0·0
4	NE	+28·0	0·707 (S4)	+19·9	0·707 (S4)	+19·9	1·0 (S8)	+28·0	0·0 (S0)	0·0	0·707 (S4)	+19·9	−0·707 (−S4)	−19·9	0·0	0·0	−1·0	−28·0
6	ENE	+22·0	0·924 (S6)	+20·3	0·383 (S2)	+8·4	0·707 (S4)	+15·0	−0·707 (−S4)	−15·6	−0·383 (−S2)	−8·4	−0·924 (−S6)	−20·3	−1·0	−22·0	0·0	0·0
8	E	+14·0	1·0 (S8)	+14·0	0·0 (S0)	0·0	0·0 (S0)	0·0	−1·0 (−S8)	−14·0	−1·0 (−S8)	−14·0	0·0 (S0)	0·0	0·0	E 0·0	1·0	+14·0
10	ESE	+4·0	0·924 (S6)	+3·7	−0·383 (−S2)	−1·5	−0·707 (−S4)	−2·8	−0·707 (−S4)	−2·8	−0·383 (−S2)	−1·5	0·924 (S6)	+3·7	1·0	+4·0	0·0	0·0
12	SE	−7·5	0·707 (S4)	−5·3	−0·707 (−S4)	+5·3	−1·0 (−S8)	+7·5	0·0 (S0)	0·0	0·707 (S4)	−5·3	0·707 (S4)	−5·3	0·0	0·0	−1·0	+7·5
14	SSE	−18·0	0·383 (S2)	−6·9	−0·924 (−S6)	+16·6	−0·707 (−S4)	+12·8	0·707 (S4)	−12·8	0·924 (S6)	−16·6	−0·383 (−S2)	+6·9	−1·0	+18·0	0·0	0·0
16	S	−24·0	0·0 (S0)	0·0	−1·0 (−S8)	+24·0	0·0 (S0)	0·0	1·0 (S8)	−24·0	0·0 (S0)	0·0	−1·0 (−S8)	+24·0	0·0	S 0·0	1·0	−24·0
18	SSW	−28·0	−0·383 (−S2)	+10·7	−0·924 (−S6)	+25·8	0·707 (S4)	−19·9	0·707 (S4)	−19·9	−0·924 (−S6)	+25·8	−0·383 (−S2)	+10·7	1·0	−28·0	0·0	0·0
20	SW	−27·0	−0·707 (−S4)	+19·2	−0·707 (−S4)	+19·2	1·0 (S8)	−27·0	0·0 (S0)	0·0	−0·707 (−S4)	+19·2	0·707 (S4)	−19·2	0·0	0·0	−1·0	+28·0
22	WSW	−23·0	−0·924 (−S6)	+21·2	−0·383 (−S2)	+8·8	0·707 (S4)	−16·3	−0·707 (−S4)	+16·3	0·383 (S2)	−8·8	0·924 (S6)	−21·2	−1·0	+23·0	0·0	0·0
24	W	−16·0	−1·0 (−S8)	+16·0	0·0 (S0)	0·0	0·0 (S0)	0·0	−1·0 (−S8)	+16·0	1·0 (S8)	−16·0	0·0 (S0)	0·0	0·0	0·0	1·0	−16·0
26	WNW	−7·0	−0·924 (−S6)	+6·5	0·383 (S2)	−2·7	−0·707 (−S4)	+5·0	−0·707 (−S4)	+5·0	0·383 (S2)	−2·7	−0·924 (−S6)	+6·5	1·0	−7·0	0·0	0·0
28	NW	+6·0	−0·707 (−S4)	−4·3	0·707 (S4)	+4·3	−1·0 (−S8)	−6·0	0·0 (S0)	0·0	−0·707 (−S4)	−4·3	−0·707 (−S4)	−4·3	0·0	0·0	−1·0	−6·0
30	NNW	+15·0	−0·383 (−S2)	−5·7	0·924 (S6)	+13·8	−0·707 (−S4)	−10·6	0·707 (S4)	+10·6	−0·924 (−S6)	−13·8	0·383 (S2)	+5·7	−1·0	−15·0	0·0	0·0

	Dev.	1×2	1×4	1×6	1×8	1×10	1×12	1×14	1×16
Positive totals	+145·0	+143·3	+200·3	+90·3	+94·9	+93·5	+94·3	+76·0	+74·5
Negative totals	−150·5	−22·2	−4·2	−82·6	−89·1	−91·4	−90·2	−72·0	−74·0
Algebraic sum	$16A = -5{\cdot}5$	$8B = +121{\cdot}1$	$8C = +196{\cdot}1$	$8D = +7{\cdot}7$	$8E = +5{\cdot}8$	$8F = +2{\cdot}1$	$8G = +4{\cdot}1$	$8H = +4{\cdot}0$	$8K = +0{\cdot}5$
Coefficients	$A = -0{\cdot}3$	$B = +15{\cdot}1$	$C = +24{\cdot}5$	$D = +1{\cdot}0$	$E = +0{\cdot}7$	$F = +0{\cdot}3$	$G = +0{\cdot}5$	$H = +0{\cdot}5$	$K = +0{\cdot}1$

Note—A, E, F, G, H and K are negligible, the vessel acquired a very large sub-permanent B and C.

$$\overline{B} = B - \frac{BD}{2}, \text{ etc.}$$

In making the tabulated calculations described above it will be realised that the numerical values of the trigonometrical ratios in columns No. 2, No. 4, No. 6, etc., keep repeating themselves. In fact only five values are used corresponding to sin 0°, sin $22\frac{1}{2}°$, sin 45°, sin $67\frac{1}{2}°$ and sin 90°, *i.e.*, 0, 0·383, 0·707, 0·924 and 1 respectively, with the signs for the appropriate quadrant attached. If we call these 0, S_2, S_4, S_6 and 1, then the sine of 10 points (ESE) equals S_6, the sine of 20 points (SW) equals $-S_4$, the sine of 24 points (W) equals -1 and so on.

Also cos $\propto$ = sin (90 $-\propto$), therefore we can write cos 2 points = S_6, cos 10 points = $-S_2$, cos 20 points = $-S_4$, cos 24 points = 0, etc.

Again, sin twice 2 points = S_4, and cos twice 8 points = -1, etc.

Thus if the value of deviation from say 0·5 to 10°, in steps of 0·5, are successively multiplied by S_2, S_4 and S_6, a Table of products can be made which will greatly facilitate the calculations. The products are required only to the first decimal place. Such a Table is contained in the *Admiralty Manual of Deviations* and reproduced below.

TABLE III
(All values are in degrees)

Deviations	Products of S_2	S_4	S_6	Deviations	Products of S_2	S_4	S_6
0·5	0·2	0·5	0·5	5·5	2·1	3·9	5·1
1·0	0·4	0·7	1·0	6·0	2·3	4·3	5·5
1·5	0·6	1·1	1·4	6·5	2·5	4·6	6·0
2·0	0·8	1·4	1·9	7·0	2·7	5·0	6·5
2·5	1·0	1·8	2·3	7·5	2·9	5·3	6·9
3·0	1·2	2·1	2·8	8·0	3·1	5·7	7·4
3·5	1·3	2·5	3·2	8·5	3·3	6·0	7·9
4·0	1·5	2·8	3·7	9·0	3·5	6·4	8·3
4·5	1·7	3·2	4·2	9·5	3·6	6·7	8·8
5·0	1·9	3·5	4·6	10·0	3·8	7·1	9·2

If the deviation is outside the limit of the Table, the "S" product may be found by combining two values inside the Table, e.g.,

$$13{\cdot}5\,S_4 = 10\,S_4 + 3{\cdot}5\,S_4 = 7{\cdot}1 + 2{\cdot}5 = 9{\cdot}6.$$

Suitable interpolation should be used when the deviation is not a multiple of $0{\cdot}5$, e.g., $3{\cdot}2\,S_6$ lies between $3{\cdot}0\,S_6$ and $3{\cdot}5\,S_6 = 3{\cdot}0$ to one decimal place.

If only eight equidistant points are used and the observations are carefully made and the values of the deviations so obtained are small, the approximate coefficients can be found to a reasonable degree of accuracy by the following rules, which will be seen to be in agreement with the method described above.

Coefficient A is the mean of the algebraic sum of the deviations on all eight points.

Coefficient B is the mean of the deviations on East and West with the sign of the deviation on West reversed.

Coefficient C is the mean of the deviations on North and South with the sign of the deviation on South reversed.

Coefficient D is the mean of the deviations on NE, SE, SW and NW with the sign of the deviation on SE and NW reversed.

Coefficient E is the mean of the deviations on North, East, South and West with the sign of the deviation on East and West reversed.

CHAPTER XVI

THEORY OF THE MECHANICAL CORRECTION OF THE COMPASS

THE mechanical correction of that part of the deviations caused by the ship's permanent magnetic field is effected by means of permanent magnets, and is in practice straightforward, but in the case of the soft-iron correctors, complications arise due to the fact that the induced magnetism in the correctors may not be wholly due to the earth's field. It may in part be due to the permanent correcting magnets or due to the compass needle system itself.

Flinders Bar. The Flinders bar is used to correct that part of the semicircular deviation caused by the excess of vertical soft iron forward or abaft the compass, but symmetrically disposed to starboard and port, *i.e.*, c rod effect.

The bar is placed, with its long axis vertical, in a container fixed usually on the fore side of the binnacle to correct a negative c. The upper end of the bar is placed so that one-twelfth of its length is above the horizontal plane through the compass-needle system. The amount of correction is varied by using longer or shorter lengths of bar. The effect of a shorter bar is less, partly due to the increased proximity of the lower end and partly due to the greater demagnetising factor of a shorter bar. (See page 26.)

As the breadth of the bar is not negligible, it has the effect of $+a$ and $-e$ rods causing a small coefficient D which increases the normal $+D$ of the ship for which the spheres are used to compensate.

Induction in the bar by the horizontal permanent correcting magnets merely augments the corrections for which these magnets are used. Provided, therefore, the bar is in position when the magnets are placed, the compensation will be satisfactory from this point of view.

Nevertheless induction due to the vertical permanent magnets, used in the heeling-error correction, cannot be considered constant, as the raising or lowering of these magnets to adjust the heeling-error correction will alter the amount of induction in the bar and upset the corrections made by the fore and aft magnets. This effect is by no means negligible. A bar 24 inch (61 cm) in length has been known to cause 9° deviation due to induction from a full "bucket" of seven heeling-error magnets with the bucket well down in the binnacle.

If the vertical soft iron is not symmetrically disposed to starboard and port of the compass, the excess to one side will cause an f rod effect. This could be compensated for by an additional Flinders bar to starboard or port of the compass as required. In practice this is neither convenient nor necessary. When the values of c and f are known, the Flinders bar normally used to correct for c is slewed to an angle with the fore and aft line, the tangent of which

is equal to $\dfrac{f}{c}$, where f is the deviation caused by the induced

part of coefficient C and c is the deviation caused by the induced part of coefficient B.

If c and f are both negative, the bar will be forward and to starboard of the compass.

If c and f are both positive, the bar will be aft and to port of the compass.

The length of Flinders bar required is not immediately determinable, as it is not possible to obtain from observations in one magnetic latitude the separate values of the P and c rod effects which go to make up coefficient B or, if necessary, the separate values of Q and f rod effects which go to make up coefficient C.

The usual procedure is, in the first instance, to estimate the length required from experience with similar ships, or, if this is not possible, then, as a rough estimate, 12 inches (30·5 cm) should be placed on the side of the compass toward the nearer end of the ship. A closer correction can then be made when observations are possible at a second place where the value of H is appreciably different from that at which the first observations and approximate correction were made.

The Admiralty Compass Observatory have published a Table showing the values of c

$$\left[\text{from the expression} \, \bar{B} = \frac{1}{\lambda}\left(c \tan \theta - \frac{P}{H} \right) \right]$$

which varying lengths of Flinders bar will correct. It should be realised that the value of c is the sine of the deviation caused by the c rod with the ship's head East by compass at a place where the dip is 45°, i.e., so that $\sin \zeta'$ and $\tan \theta$ are both equal to unity.

The method of splitting coefficient B and/or coefficient C into the two parts is given, together with worked examples, in the

Appendix at the end of the book. (Page 152, Examples (3) and (4).)

The Soft-Iron Spheres. The spheres correct the quadrantal deviations which, in a well-placed compass, are due only to symmetrically disposed horizontal soft iron.

They usually correct a coefficient $+D$ due to the excess of $-e$ rod effect over that of the $-a$ rod effect, owing to the athwartship ends of the soft iron being nearer to the compass than those in the fore and aft direction.

The spheres also increase the value of λ, the mean of the ratio $\dfrac{H'}{H}$ for all headings of the ship, but it should be noted, however, that the fore and aft component of the earth's induction in the spheres is a $-a$ rod which augments the $-a$ rod of the ship. The athwartship component, however, is a $+e$ rod which decreases the $-e$ rod of the ship, and to this extent is a factor in increasing the value of λ. The $+e$ rod effect of the spheres, being "end on" to the compass needle, is twice that of the $-a$ rod which is "broadside on" to the compass needle. (See page 30.)

When the spheres are correctly placed the $-e$ rod remaining $(-e_2)$ will be equal to the augmented $-a$ rod $(-a_2)$, and

$$D = \frac{(-a_2 + e_2)}{2\lambda} = 0. \quad \text{(See page 74.)}$$

The spheres also correct for the heeling error caused by that part of the $-e$ rod which they have corrected for deviation. They do not correct for the heeling error caused by the e_2 rod. (See heeling-error correction, page 75.)

As in the case of the Flinders bar, the spheres have secondary effects due to induction in them by the permanent magnets placed in the binnacle, and to their own permanent magnetism arising from the iron not being purely soft in character. These effects are normally small, and in the case of the vertical magnets usually negligible. Nevertheless, the spheres should be marked after being placed to ensure that the permanent poles in them shall always remain in the same position relative to the compass needle. The effect of induction by the permanent magnets is simply to alter the corrections for which the magnets are used, while that due to the permanent magnetism in the spheres is supplementary to the ship's magnetism and corrected with it. These effects necessitate the placing of the spheres before the correction for permanent magnetism is made.

The effect of induction by the compass needles cannot be treated in the same way as that due to the permanent magnets, as the former is of a quadrantal nature due to the fact that its value will vary with change of ship's head. The spheres, therefore, give two "D" effects, one of a soft-iron nature and the other of a hard-iron nature, the former, of course, having the greater value. When the spheres are correctly placed these two values, which may be written $(D^s + D_m)$, are equal to the D of the ship.

With change of magnetic latitude, however, the hard-iron effect will vary inversely as H, the earth's horizontal force. Thus, if the spheres are correctly placed at a place where the earth's horizontal force is equal to H, then

$$(D_s + D_m) = D.$$

If the ship now sails to a place where the horizontal force is H', then the deviation due to the ship's soft iron remains the same. Thus D is constant, but the correcting effect due to the spheres will become

$$\left(D_s + \frac{H}{H'} D_m\right),$$

and a deviation will therefore appear equal to

$$\left(D_s + D_m\right) - \left(D_s + \frac{H}{H'} D_m\right)$$

$$= D_s + D_m - D_s - \frac{H}{H'} D_m$$

$$= D_m\left(1 - \frac{H}{H'}\right).$$

From the above reasoning it will be seen that with change of magnetic latitude, although the D of the ship remains constant, some slight adjustment of the spheres may still be necessary if close correction of the compass is desired.

The above facts should be borne in mind when selecting compass cards and also when dealing with the adjustment of compasses on board ship. The shorter the needles in the system the less will be the induction in the spheres, as will be the case with larger spheres at a greater distance than would otherwise be required. The mathematical theory of induction in the spheres is dealt with at the end of this chapter together with the proof of the "angle of slew" for the spheres when a coefficient E is present, the rule for which is given below.

If, due to the unsymmetrical distribution of soft iron, there is a coefficient E, the spheres must be slewed to an angle from the athwartship plane such that $\dfrac{E}{D}$ is the tangent of *twice* that angle. This assumes a normal positive D. If, on the other hand, D is negative, then the angle of slew must be measured from the fore and aft plane through the compass.

Whether D is positive or negative if E is positive, the port sphere will be in the direction of the port bow. If E is negative, then the starboard sphere will be in the direction of the starboard bow.

The maximum deviation effect of the spheres when slewed is equal to

$$\sqrt{E^2 + D^2},$$

this value is required if Tables published by the Admiralty Compass Observatory are used. These Tables are made from experiment, and show the amount of deviation which will be corrected by spheres of different diameters at varying distances from the compass. The distance used in the latest Tables is from the centre of the compass to the centre of each sphere as a port and starboard sphere is assumed to be required. It can be taken, however, that one sphere has half the effect of two.

Effect of Swinging a Ship Too Quickly. This effect was first noticed by M. Gaussin and carries his name, *i.e.*, "Gaussin Error." Gaussin assumed that the error was due to a lag in the molecular change in direction in soft iron due to hysteresis as the ship was swung in azimuth.

The modern theory is that electric eddy currents set up when a ship turns from one course to another (*i.e.*, is linked with a changing number of lines of force) causes the magnetism of the ship to take an appreciable time to settle down to its normal value after change of course. The resulting effect is the same in either case, and may be described as follows.

Consider a ship in which the soft iron is symmetrically placed so that coefficients $\overline{A}$ and $\overline{E}$ are zero, and so that only the effects on the a and e rods need be regarded.

If the ship is swung rapidly to starboard from North through to East and there is a lag in the change in the induction in the a rod, it will retain some of the magnetism induced when on North while the ship is heading East. A $+a$ rod would give the added effect of a $-b'$ rod. (See *Fig.* 59.)

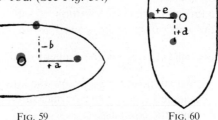

FIG. 59   FIG. 60

By the same reasoning, if the ship is again swung rapidly to starboard from East through to South, a $+e$ rod would give the added effect of a $+d'$ rod. (See *Fig.* 60.)

The effect of the d' and b' rods will be to cause apparent coefficients A' and E', and if s is the small angle of lag, then

the deviation on North, $\delta_N = A' + E' = \dfrac{-se}{2\lambda}$

and the deviation on East, $\delta_E = A' - E' = \dfrac{-sa}{\lambda}.$

For a positive value of D and a value of λ less than unity, if the ship is swung to starboard (clockwise), the effect is to cause an additional westerly deviation on all courses, that on North and South being greater than that on East and West. If the ship is swung to port (anticlockwise), then the added deviation will be easterly.

In order to avoid this error when swinging ship for deviations or for compass correction, at least forty minutes should be taken for a complete swing, and what is more important, the ship should be steadied on each course for, say, two minutes, before the observation for deviation is made.

Retentive Error. When a ship has been steering one course for a considerable period of time, the ship's sub-permanent magnetism tends to align itself in the direction of the magnetic meridian. For instance, if the ship steers an easterly course for a long time, due to the various vibrations, the sub-permanent molecules tend to align themselves in the direction of the earth's field, causing a red sub-permanent pole to port of the compass and a blue sub-permanent pole to starboard of the compass. (See *Fig.* 61.)

If then the vessel alters course to starboard and steers a southerly course, an added westerly deviation will be present. Conversely, on northerly courses an added easterly deviation will appear.

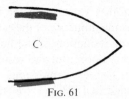

FIG. 61

Similarly, if the vessel steered North for a considerable time, she would acquire a red sub-permanent pole in the bow and a blue sub-permanent pole aft. Altering course to the eastward would then cause an additional westerly deviation, and altering course to the westward would cause an additional easterly deviation.

The effect from steering northerly or southerly courses is generally less than that from steering easterly or westerly courses, due to the sub-permanent poles being nearer the compass in the latter case.

This error is usually referred to as "retentive error", and has the effect of altering the values of the permanent parts of coefficients B and C, and is a semicircular deviation. Its effect decreases with time, depending upon the permanence of the character of the magnetism concerned.

It must be anticipated and allowed for until its effect wears off. In practice it is important that observations for deviations on the new course concerned be made either at an opportune moment before the course is finally altered or as soon after as possible, and then checked at such intervals as conditions will allow.

Magnetic Screening. If a compass is surrounded by soft iron, the directive force is reduced, due to the earth's lines of force tending to concentrate in the material of higher permeability. (See *Fig.* 62.)

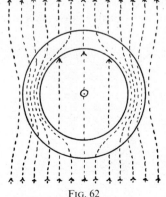

FIG. 62

The relative permeability varies with the inducing field, but for the iron of a ship under the influence of the earth's field is about 100.

The calculation of the reduction of the field due to screening is outside the scope of this book, but the results for a sphere and a cylinder are of interest. The two expressions are due to M. du Bois. They were first published in 1898 and are still accepted.

He states that the field inside a hollow sphere is given by

$$H' = \frac{H}{1 + \frac{2}{9}(\mu - 2)\left(1 - \frac{r^3}{R^3}\right)}$$

where H is the external field (in our case, of that of the earth), μ is the permeability of the material, and r and R are the internal and external radius of the sphere respectively.

Thus, if the ratio of r to R is as $9:10$, then the field inside a hollow sphere of permeability 100 is approximately one-seventh of the earth's field, and if the ratio of r to R is as $99:100$, then the field is approximately eight-thirteenths or roughly two-thirds of the earth's field.

For a cylinder with its axis at right angles to the field the internal field is given by

$$H' = \frac{H}{1 + \frac{1}{4}(\mu - 2)\left(1 - \frac{r^2}{R^2}\right)}$$

Thus, for a ratio of r to R as $9:10$, the field inside a hollow cylinder of permeability 100 is approximately two-elevenths of the earth's field, and if the ratio of r to R is as $99:100$, then the internal field is approximately two-thirds of the earth's field.

Magnetic Latitude. If the earth be considered as a sphere with a short magnet at the centre whose axis is in the direction of

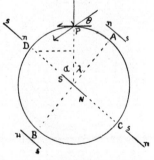

FIG. 63

the line joining the magnetic poles and its polarity consistent with the effects which are known to exist, see *Fig.* 63, then for such a magnetic condition a dip needle would take up a vertical position at points *C* and *D* and a horizontal position at points *A* and *B*. The former correspond to the Magnetic Poles and the latter lie in the Magnetic Equator. At a point *P* on the surface the angle subtended at the centre by the arc $AP = \lambda$ = Magnetic Latitude. Let the angle subtended by the arc $CP = \alpha$. Then $\lambda = (90 - \alpha)$. Let *R* be the radius of the sphere.

The component of the moment of the magnet along a radius through $P = m \cos \alpha = m \sin \lambda$ where *m* is the magnetic moment of the magnet *NS*.

The field at *P* due to this

$$= \frac{2m \sin \lambda}{4\pi\mu_0 R^3}$$

and is vertical and "end on".

The component of the moment of the magnet perpendicular to the radius through *P* is $m \sin \alpha = m \cos \lambda$.

The field at *P* due to this

$$= \frac{m \cos \lambda}{4\pi\mu_0 R^3}$$

and is horizontal and "broadside on".

If θ is the angle of Dip at *P*,

then
$$\text{Tan } \theta = \frac{2m \sin \lambda}{4\pi\mu_0 R^3} \times \frac{4\pi\mu_0 R^3}{m \cos \lambda}$$

$$= 2 \frac{\sin \lambda}{\cos \lambda}$$

$$= 2 \tan \lambda.$$

Thus   Tan Dip = 2 tan Magnetic Latitude.

Determination of λ and λ_2. It has been shown that the value of λ, the ratio of the mean directive force at the compass position compared with that of the earth, is due entirely to the influence of horizontal soft iron. Other factors causing deviation increase the directive force on some directions of the ship's head and equally decrease it on the diametrically opposite points. The effect of continuous horizontal soft iron is to decrease the directive force on all points. When the spheres are placed, the value of the $-a$ rod is increased but the value of the $-e$ rod is decreased, and the new value of a is equal to the new value of e, so that $a_2 = e_2$.

$$\lambda = 1 + \frac{a + e}{2}$$

whence

$$\lambda_2 = 1 + \frac{a_2 + e_2}{2} = 1 + \frac{2e_2}{2}$$

$$= 1 + e_2.$$

On page 102 it was seen that $1 + e_2 = \mu_2$, therefore if λ_2 is known the value of the ship's "multiplier" is known.

As e is invariably negative, the value of λ (or λ_2) is less than unity. That is, the directive force at the compass position is always less than if it were due to the earth's force alone. λ_2 is the best value for the directive force ratio that can be obtained at the compass position.

The value of λ or λ_2 may be found by means of a horizontal vibrating needle.

The equation for the experiment may be written

$$T = 2\pi \sqrt{\frac{I}{MH}} \quad \text{(see page 50),}$$

where T is the period of the needle, I is the Moment of Inertia of the needle about an axis through its c.g. perpendicular to its length, M is the Magnetic Moment of the needle, and H is the strength of field in which the needle vibrates. In our case H is the earth's field and H_1 is the field at the compass position.

If the period of the needle is found in two different fields, H and H_1, we can write

$$T = 2\pi \sqrt{\frac{I}{MH}} \quad\quad (a)$$

and

$$T_1 = 2\pi \sqrt{\frac{I}{MH_1}} \quad\quad (b)$$

Dividing (a) by (b), 2π, I and M cancel (the same needle being used for both experiments), and we get

$$\frac{T}{T_1} = \sqrt{\frac{\dfrac{1}{H}}{\dfrac{1}{H_1}}}$$

or

$$\frac{T^2}{T_1^2} = \frac{H_1}{H}.$$

From equation 7 (page 70), it was seen that the mean value of $\frac{H_1}{H} \cos \delta = \lambda$, and therefore the mean value of $\frac{T^2}{T_1^2} \cos \delta = \lambda$.

Hence, if a vibrating needle is taken ashore to a position free from local magnetic disturbance and made to oscillate as described on page 49, in the earth's field H, the period T due to H can be found. The oscillations should be of small amplitude, and the time of at least ten full oscillations should be taken.

If the needle is then taken on board and placed in the position of the compass (the card or bowl being unshipped) and the experiment repeated on at least four equidistant headings, usually the cardinal points, the mean value of the period so found will be the mean value of T_1 due to H_1, the magnetic field at the compass position.

The ship's head should be magnetic in each case or the parts of the field used will not be symmetrical if the deviations are appreciable, and in order to compute λ, the mean value of $\frac{H_1}{H} \cos \delta$, it is

necessary to multiply the T^2 found on each heading by the cosine of the deviation for the ship's head concerned before taking the mean.

If the deviations are small, say 1° or 2°, they can be ignored, as the cosine is then for all practical purposes unity. Also, if exactly the same number of oscillations is timed in each case, T and T_1 can be taken as the time of the number of oscillations, instead of the period of one complete oscillation.

The experiment described above may be used in the case of new ships for experimental purposes to find the most suitable position for the standard compass, i.e., the position where λ is greatest.

In practice the experiment is made after the compass has been corrected. In this case the value obtained is λ_2, and is used as the ship's "multiplier".

From the above it is obvious that if H, the earth's force, is known (it can be found by reference to the Horizontal Force chart), then H_1 on any particular ship's head may be found if required. For instance, on North, say, we can write

$$H_N = H \times \frac{T^2}{T_N^2}$$

or on South $$H_S = H \times \frac{T^2}{T_S^2}.$$

Therefore, if suitable correctors were placed in position and adjusted so that $T_N^2 = T_S^2$, then the directive force on North and South would be equalised.

Hence, by means of a number of experiments with the vibrating needle, the directive force could be equalised on all points and the compass corrected for deviations. This would be a long and tedious process, and is never adopted in practice.

It will be seen subsequently that from the four results obtained on the cardinal points for the determination of λ, Coefficients B, C and D could be found if desired.

The Deflector. There are various types of deflector, the two best-known being the Thompson and the de Colongue.

The Thompson deflector consists of a hinged magnet system composed of two pairs of magnets each pair hinged with their opposite poles together. By means of a screw drive the distance of the lower ends of each pair from each other may be varied by turning the milled head of the screw. The greater the distance between the opposite lower poles of the system, the greater the magnetic moment of the system.

The framework on which the system is mounted fits on to the top of the compass bowl. It is carefully centred and may be turned in azimuth. A pointer shows the direction of the magnetic field of the system. On the pointer is etched a graduated scale over which an indicator moves as the moment of the magnet system is varied. The reading from the scale when the adjustment has been made is proportional to the directive force H_1, for the particular heading on which the measurement is made.

To correct the compass using the deflector, four observations are made, that is, with the ship's head on the cardinal points—North, East, South and West by compass. It is necessary that the ship's head when once steadied on a point by the compass concerned is kept on a steady course by means of the steering compass or otherwise. On each of the headings the deflector is placed on the compass with the blue poles of the system over the north point of the compass, and then turned in azimuth, while the field strength is varied until the card has been deflected through 90°, the pointer being kept over some fixed reading of the deflected compass card (usually 80° or E by N). Thus, if the ship is heading North, then when the adjustment is completed the West point of the card will be opposite the lubber point, and the pointer of the instrument will be over 80° or E by N, *i.e.*, will be pointing within about 10° from right aft.

Referring to page 45, it will be seen that theoretically the pointer should be over 90° on the card. The deflection would then be 90° with the magnet end-on and at right angles to the compass needle. The field of the instrument would then be equal and opposite to the part of the ship's field under consideration. In practice this is an impossibility, but the nearer to a 90° card reading the pointer is placed, the less will be the instrumental error in the correction, and 80° is about as near as one can get. It must be emphasised that the same reading must be used for each observation and the deflection of the card must be always 90°. In some textbooks this deflection is referred to as "normal deflection", and it must be stressed that "normal" in this context is used in the strictly mathematical sense and means "at right angles". The errors involved in using values other than 90° and 80° are discussed later in the chapter.

The Flinders bar must be in place and the spheres should be in their approximate positions.

When the observations have been made on North and South by compass the readings taken from the instrument, say R_N and R_S, will be proportional to the field strength at the compass position on those headings respectively. To equalise those fields we require that $R_N = R_S$. If fore and aft magnets are introduced into the binnacle, the R_N will be increased by exactly the same amount as the R_S is decreased, or *vice versa*. Hence the reading on the scale of the deflector is adjusted to read $\dfrac{R_N + R_S}{2}$ while the ship is on one of these headings and fore and aft magnets are inserted and adjusted so that the deflection returns to 90° with the pointer over the same card reading as before, the desired result will be attained and coefficient B will be corrected. If R_N is the greater reading, the magnets will be placed red ends forward and *vice versa*.

Similarly, to correct coefficient C, the readings on East and West, R_E and R_W, must be made equal. Therefore if we adjust the scale reading to $\dfrac{R_E + R_W}{2}$ with the ship on one of these headings, and insert athwartship magnets and adjust them until the deflection of the card is again 90° with the pointer at the same card reading, C will be corrected. If R_E is the greater reading, the magnets must be placed red ends to port, and *vice versa*.

With B and C corrected, the directive force on North and South and on East and West will have been equalised. We require that the equalised directive force on North and South shall be equal to the equalised directive force on East and West, in other words, that

$$\frac{R_N + R_S}{2} = \frac{R_E + R_W}{2}.$$

The scale reading must thus be adjusted to the mean of these two means and the spheres moved in or out until the 90° deflection is again maintained with the pointer over the same card reading. This will complete the correction of coefficient D. If $\dfrac{R_N + R_S}{2}$ is the greater reading, the spheres must be moved in, and *vice versa*. This adjustment is made with the ship's head on either East or West.

The de Colongue Deflector. This instrument consists of a non-magnetic base plate carrying a pointer and to which may be fitted a vertical rod with its axis in line with the pivot.

The vertical rod carries the main and auxiliary magnet systems. The main magnet system is so mounted that its centre point can be moved up and down the rod, but so that the system cannot be rotated round the rod. Its direction is indicated by the pointer on the base, and its position on the vertical rod may be read off from a scale on the rod. The auxiliary magnet is mounted at the base of the rod at right angles to the vertical plane defined by the magnetic axis of the main magnets and the axis of the rod, so that the moment of the auxiliary magnet is 90° to the right, *i.e.*, clockwise, of the magnetic moment of the main system.

To use the deflector, the ship's head is maintained on the required heading, *i.e.*, North, East, South or West, by means of a steering compass or otherwise. The non-magnetic base plate is fitted to the rim of the compass bowl and clamped with the pointer accurately situated over the South point of the compass card. During this process the magnetic parts of the instrument are kept at least 8 feet or more away from the compass.

When the base plate has been clamped in position the magnetic parts are mounted on it with the red end of the main magnet system toward North in exactly the opposite direction to the pointer. The main magnet is then adjusted up or down the rod until the compass aligns itself with the field of the auxiliary magnet.

In this position the main magnet system has obviously cancelled the directive force of the earth. It is also clear that the auxiliary magnet should be weak, and that the weaker the magnet the more sensitive the adjustment becomes.

The position of the main magnet system is then read off the scale on the vertical rod.

This procedure is repeated on each of the headings, and the readings R_N, R_E, R_S, R_W so obtained are then used to make the corrections of coefficients B, C and D as described for the Thompson deflector.

The chief advantages of this type of deflector are that the angle of deflection can only be $90°$, as the auxiliary magnet is mechanically fixed at right angles to the main system, thus the mistake of using any other angle cannot be made; the setting of the instrument is made by one action only, the sliding of the main system to its best position on the vertical rod. Furthermore, the errors involved are less than those of the Thompson type of deflector.

To Determine the Coefficients by means of the observations obtained using the vibrating needle or the deflector:

Equation 9 (see page 74) may be written to a first order accuracy in terms of the approximate coefficients thus:

$$\frac{H'}{\lambda H} \cos \delta = 1 + \sin B° \cos \zeta' - \sin C° \sin \zeta' + \sin D° \cos 2\zeta'$$

$$- \sin E° \sin 2\zeta' \qquad (9a)$$

where $B°$, $C°$, $D°$ and $E°$ are the approximate coefficients in terms of their corresponding deviations. (See page 85.)

λ may be found by means of the vibrating needle as previously described (page 121, *et seq.*) or in a similar manner using the deflector, but in this case the compass in its bowl must be landed at a place free from local magnetic interference and an observation made. Then, calling this reading R_A, it will correspond to $\dfrac{1}{T^2}$, and the four readings of the deflector taken on board, *i.e.*, R_N, R_E, R_S and R_W will correspond respectively to

$$\frac{1}{T_N^2}, \frac{1}{T_E^2}, \frac{1}{T_S^2} \quad \text{and} \quad \frac{1}{T_W^2},$$

the four periods found on board with the vibrating needle.

If the deviations are assumed to be small, so that $\cos \delta = 1$, we can write

$$kR_N = \frac{H'_N}{\lambda H} = 1 + \sin B° + \sin D° \qquad (1d)$$

(see note overleaf)

$$kR_S = \frac{H'_S}{\lambda H} = 1 - \sin B° + \sin D° \qquad (2d)$$

$$kR_E = \frac{H'_E}{H} = 1 - \sin C° - \sin D° \qquad (3d)$$

$$kR_W = \frac{H'_W}{\lambda H} = 1 + \sin C° - \sin D° \qquad (4d)$$

where k is the constant of the particular instrument used for the particular values of λ and H which will reduce the scale reading to terms of λH.

Note. Equation $(1d)$ (for the ship's head North) written in full is as follows:

$$kR_N = \frac{H'_N}{\lambda H} = 1 + \sin B° \cos \zeta' - \sin C° \sin \zeta' + \sin D° \cos 2\zeta'$$

$$- \sin E° \sin 2\zeta' \quad \text{(where } \zeta' = 0°\text{)}.$$

But $\cos 0° = 1$, $\sin 0° = 0$ and twice $0 = 0$.

Hence $\sin B° \cos 0° = \sin B°$, $\sin C° \sin 0° = 0$, $\sin D° \cos 0° = \sin D°$ and $\sin E° \sin 0° = 0$. The same reasoning applies to equations $(2d)$, $(3d)$ and $(4d)$.

Adding the four equations we get

$$k(R_N + R_S + R_E + R_W) = 4$$

$$k = \frac{4}{R_N + R_S + R_E + R_W} \qquad (5d)$$

The value of k being known, $B°$, $C°$ and $D°$ may be found as follows. Subtract $(2d)$ from $(1d)$ and we get:

$$k(R_N - R_S) = 2 \sin B°$$

$$\sin B° = \frac{k}{2}(R_N - R_S). \qquad (6d)$$

Subtract $(3d)$ from $(4d)$ and we get

$$k(R_W - R_E) = 2 \sin C°$$

$$\sin C° = \frac{k}{2}(R_W - R_E). \qquad (7d)$$

From the sum of $(1d)$ and $(2d)$ subtract the sum of $(3d)$ and $(4d)$ and we get

$$k[(R_N + R_S) - (R_E + R_W)] = 4 \sin D°$$

$$\sin D° = \frac{k}{4}[(R_N + R_S) - (R_E + R_W)]. \qquad (8d)$$

To determine the value of $E°$, four more observations are required with the ship's head on NE, SE, SW and NW. Calling the readings on these headings R_{NE}, R_{SE}, R_{SW} and R_{NW} respectively, and remembering that $\sin 45 = \dfrac{1}{\sqrt{2}}$, $\cos 45 = \dfrac{1}{\sqrt{2}}$, sin twice $45 = 0$, cos twice $45 = 1$, also that $\sin 225 = -\sin 45$, $\sin 315 = -\sin 45$, $\cos 135 = -\cos 45$ and $\cos 225 = -\cos 45$, the following equations may be written:

$$kR_{NE} = \frac{H'_{NE}}{\lambda H} = 1 + \sin B° \cos 45 - \sin C° \sin 45 - \sin E°$$

$$= 1 + \frac{\sin B°}{\sqrt{2}} - \frac{\sin C°}{\sqrt{2}} - \sin E° \tag{9d}$$

$$kR_{SE} = \frac{H'_{SE}}{\lambda H} = 1 + \sin B° \cos 135 - \sin C° \sin 135 + \sin E°$$

$$= 1 - \frac{\sin B°}{\sqrt{2}} - \frac{\sin C°}{\sqrt{2}} + \sin E° \tag{10d}$$

$$kR_{SW} = \frac{H'_{SW}}{\lambda H} = 1 + \sin B° \cos 225 - \sin C° \sin 225 - \sin E°$$

$$= 1 - \frac{\sin B°}{\sqrt{2}} + \frac{\sin C°}{\sqrt{2}} - \sin E° \tag{11d}$$

$$kR_{NW} = \frac{H'_{NW}}{\lambda H} = 1 + \sin B° \cos 315 - \sin C° \sin 315 + \sin E°$$

$$= 1 + \frac{\sin B°}{\sqrt{2}} + \frac{\sin C°}{\sqrt{2}} + \sin E°. \tag{12d}$$

From the sum of (10d) and (12d) subtract the sum of (9d) and (11d) and we get

$$k[(R_{SE} + R_{NW}) - (R_{NE} + R_{SW})] = 4 \sin E°$$

$$\sin E° = \frac{k}{4}[(R_{SE} + R_{NW}) - (R_{NE} + R_{SW})]. \tag{13d}$$

Coefficient $A°$ cannot be found by means of deflector observations, as it does not contribute to directive force at the compass position.

If the deviations on the various headings is not negligible, then $\cos \delta$ is less than unity, and equation (1d), for instance, should read from which it will be seen that, in these circumstances, each reading

$$kR_N \cos \delta_N = \frac{H'_N \cos \delta_N}{\lambda H} = 1 + \sin B° + \sin D°,$$

—R_N, R_E, R_S, R_W, R_{NE}, etc.—should first be multiplied by the cosine of the appropriate deviation for the particular direction of the ship's head involved.

Summary

(1) In the case of the Thompson deflector, it is essential that the compass shall be deflected through 90°, and that the pointer of the instrument shall be directed over a reading of at least 80°, or say E by N, on the card at this deflection, and that the same angle shall be used throughout the swing.

(2) To correct the compass:

(a) The Flinders bar and the spheres are first placed in position, the latter temporarily.

(b) The ship's head must be steadied on the requisite point by the compass which is being corrected, and then maintained on that course by other means (steering compass) while the observation is being made.

(c) To correct Coefficient B. Adjust the scale reading of the instrument to the mean of the readings on North and South while heading on one of those points and insert fore and aft magnets, adjusting them to obtain the 90° deflection with the pointer over E by N of the card. If the reading on North is the greater, the magnets must have their red poles forward, and if the lesser then red poles aft.

(d) To correct Coefficient C. Adjust the reading of the scale to the mean of the readings on East and West while heading on one of these points and insert athwartship magnets, adjusting them to obtain the 90° deflection with the pointer over E by N. If the reading on East is the greater, the magnets must have their red poles to port, and if the lesser then red poles to starboard.

(e) To correct Coefficient D. Adjust the scale reading of the instrument to the mean of the above two means and, while heading East or West, move the spheres to obtain the 90° deflection with the pointer over E by N. If the mean of North and South readings is the greater, the spheres must be moved in, and if the lesser then the spheres must be moved out.

(3) To evaluate λ. Obtain an additional observation with the compass and bowl landed at a place free from local magnetic fields. Multiply each of the four readings obtained on board by the cosine of the respective deviation (if the deviations are large and are known), mean the results, and divide this by the reading obtained on shore.

(4) To evaluate the Coefficients $B°$, $C°$ and $D°$:

(a) Divide 4 by the sum of the four readings on North, East, South and West, this will give the constant of the instrument for the conditions concerned.

(b) Subtract the reading on South from the reading on North and multiply the result by half the constant obtained in (a) above. This will give the sine of Coefficient $B°$. If this value is negative, i.e., if South is the greater reading, then B is negative.

(c) Subtract the reading on East from the reading on West and multiply the result by half the constant found in (a) above. This will give the sine of Coefficient $C°$. If this value is negative, i.e., if East is the greater reading, then C is negative.

(d) Subtract the sum of the readings on East and West from the sum of the readings on North and South and multiply by one-quarter the constant obtained in (a) above. This will give the sine of Coefficient $D°$. If this value is negative, then the D showing is negative (the spheres may be in place overcorrecting).

(5) To correct Coefficient E:

(a) $D°$ must first be evaluated as in 4(d) above.

(b) Then $E°$ must be evaluated by obtaining readings on the inter-cardinal points. Subtract the sum of the readings on NE and SW from the sum of the readings on SE and NW and multiply the result by one-quarter of the constant found in 4(a) above. This will give the sine of Coefficient $E°$. If this value is negative, then E is negative.

(c) If the spheres are in place for approximate D, note their size and the distance at which they are fitted from the compass, and from the Admiralty tables find the $D°$ already corrected, add this (algebraically) to the $D°$ found above, and the result will be the "Total $D°$". Then half the angle of which $\dfrac{E°}{\text{Total } D°}$ is the tangent will be the angle of slew. Find the value of $\sqrt{E^2 + D^2}$ and then, from the tables, find the distance at which to place the spheres (see also page 115).

Errors of the Deflector. (See note below.)

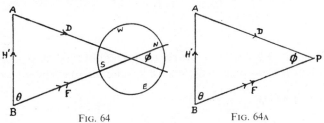

FIG. 64   FIG. 64A

Note. "D" denotes the scale reading and must not be confused with "Coefficient D" used elsewhere in the text.

Errors in D (the scale reading) due to errors in ϕ. *Figure* 64 represents diagrammatically the forces and angles involved when the deflector produces a magnetic force D, causing a clockwise deflection θ when the field of the deflector indicated by the pointer is directed to an angle ϕ clockwise from the North point of the compass card.

If no consideration is given to errors it might appear that any configuration of the triangle of forces (*Fig.* 64A) would be satisfactory provided that it was repeated on each heading,

$$\text{for} \quad \frac{D}{\sin \theta} = \frac{H'}{\sin \phi}, \quad \text{from which} \quad D = H' \frac{\sin \theta}{\sin \phi},$$

θ and ϕ being constant for the swing concerned, D is directly proportional to H', so that variations in H' on the different headings will be assessed from the variations of the readings of D on the deflector.

The angle ϕ is assessed by deciding when the pointer on the glass of the compass bowl is in line with a reading on the card, which is about half an inch below the glass.

Also, the adjustment of ϕ requires an alteration of the setting of the instrument and an alteration of the direction of the pointer with reference to the lubber point, both of which cause ϕ to alter.

The operation of the instrument consists not merely of reading the angle ϕ, but of making it have a specified reading without upsetting θ. If θ is kept as near 90° as possible, the error is reduced to a minimum. But practical experience shows that it is difficult to be sure that ϕ is less than 2° in error.

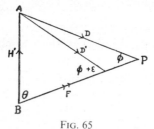

FIG. 65

In *Fig.* 65, ϕ has been adjusted as $(\phi + \varepsilon)$ but read as ϕ, causing the vector D to change to D', since θ has not altered. The fractional error in D will be $\dfrac{D' - D}{D}$.

$$\frac{D}{\sin \theta} = \frac{H'}{\sin \phi} \quad \text{and} \quad \frac{D'}{\sin \theta} = \frac{H'}{\sin (\phi + \varepsilon)},$$

from which, after some modifications, it can be shown that to second order accuracy the fractional error in D,

$$\frac{D' - D}{D} = \frac{-\sin \varepsilon}{\tan \phi + \sin \varepsilon}.$$

If we assume expert operation of the instrument, and that the error is $1°$, i.e., $\varepsilon = 1°$,

then if $\phi = 80°$, the error in D is 0.3%,
 if $\phi = 60°$, the error in D is 1.0%,
 if $\phi = 40°$, the error in D is 2.0%.

Hence from this point of view ϕ should be kept as large as possible.

Errors in D due to Errors in θ. The angle θ is the difference between the reading of the card opposite the lubber point before and after deflection. (If the reading before deflection was North, ie., the direction of the ship's head, then, after deflection clockwise, the reading opposite the lubber point should be West.) These two readings are subject to observational error, and the difference between them is also subject to any changes which have occurred in the ship's head during the operation of setting the instrument.

Let the accumulative error in θ be α (*Fig. 66*).

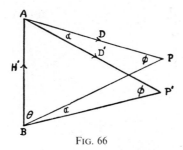

FIG. 66

The fractional error in D due to the error in θ is $\dfrac{D' - D}{D}$.

In $\triangle ABP$ $$\frac{D}{\sin \theta} = \frac{H'}{\sin \phi}$$

and in $\triangle ABP'$ $$\frac{D'}{\sin (\theta + \alpha)} = \frac{H'}{\sin \phi}$$

from which, after some modifications, it can be shown that

$$\frac{D' - D}{D} = \cot \theta \sin \alpha + \cos \alpha - 1.$$

If $\theta = 90°$, $\cot \theta = 0$, and the error is reduced to $\cos \alpha - 1$.

If α is negative, the error in D is slightly higher than when α is positive, as $\cot \theta \sin \alpha$ is then negative.

If $\alpha = -1°$ and $\theta = 90°$, the error in D is $-0·02\%$.

If $\alpha = -1°$ and $\theta = 60°$, the error in D is $-1·0\%$.

If $\alpha = -5°$ and $\theta = 90°$, the error in D is $-0·38\%$.

If $\alpha = -5°$ and $\theta = 60°$, the error in D is $-5·4\%$.

If $\alpha = -10°$ and $\theta = 90°$, the error in D is $-1·5\%$.

If $\alpha = -10°$ and $\theta = 60°$, the error in D is $-11·2\%$.

If $\theta = 40°$, the percentage error for $\theta = 60°$ is doubled, which illustrates the remarkable rate at which the error increases if θ is allowed to depart from its proper value of $90°$.

Effect of Normal Yaw. In the case of yaw of the ship's head in a seaway, the deflector may be set to some particular value of D and left to lie on the compass bowl, so following the yaw of the ship.

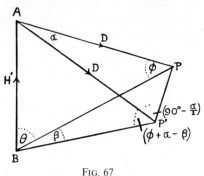

FIG. 67

In *Fig.* 67, as a result of yaw of say $\alpha°$, the vector D changes position from AP to AP' because the deflector moves with the ship. As a result the deflection θ is increased by angle β, but the lubber point has moved round through angle α, so that the change in the reading opposite the lubber point is $(\alpha - \beta)$. Therefore the apparent value of θ changes from θ to $(\theta + \alpha - \beta)$ when the yaw is α.

If θ is $90°$, it can be shown that

$$\alpha - \beta = \frac{\alpha}{2}\left[\frac{-\alpha}{\cot \phi - \alpha}\right] \text{radians.}$$

If $\theta = 90°$ and $\phi = 80°$ for 2° of yaw $(\alpha - \beta) = -0.2°$.

If $\theta = 90°$ and $\phi = 40°$ for 2° of yaw $(\alpha - \beta) = 0.0°$.

If $\theta = 90°$ and $\phi = 80°$ for 5° of yaw $(\alpha - \beta) = -2.5°$.

If $\theta = 90°$ and $\phi = 40°$ for 5° of yaw $(\alpha - \beta) = -0.2°$.

These results would make it appear that there is an argument for decreasing the angle ϕ if the vessel is yawing. This would only be true if the yaw was so slow as to be almost imperceptible. The effect of the rate of the yaw completely overshadows any gain produced by decreasing ϕ below 80°.

Inertial Effect. It is part of the object of good compass design to ensure that there should be no response to any force whose period is equal to that of the yaw, pitch, or roll of the ship. This is achieved by having a weak magnetic moment and a large moment of inertia.

Under these conditions unless, as stated above, the yaw is no more than an imperceptible creep, the uncertainty in the values of both θ and ϕ become effectively equal to the full amount of the yaw.

Thus, if say 2° of yaw be taken as good conditions, the combined effect of errors in setting in θ and ϕ would produce an error in D of

$$1\% \text{ using } \phi = 80° \qquad (\theta = 90°)$$

or $$3\% \text{ using } \phi = 60°.$$

If conditions were bad, it is still worth while using $\phi = 80°$, even if by so doing the values of θ and ϕ cannot be adjusted to nearer than 6° with certainty, for in spite of this the total error will hardly exceed 3%. Reduction of ϕ from 80° to 60° would increase this percentage to 8%.

The Effect of the Errors discussed above is to Leave Unknown Residual Deviations. There will be an error in each of the corrections for Coefficients B, C and D, and no matter what is the sign in each case, there will always be one intercardinal point on which all the errors will have the same sign.

Assuming expert manipulation of the instrument, under good conditions it is reasonable to assume that the probable maximum deviation caused by errors introduced by the instrument is about 2°, and under bad conditions it is about 4° or 5°.

These errors are unpredictable in sign, so there is no means of telling on which of the intercardinal headings the maximum deviation will occur. Nor can it be forecast how these deviations will add with other deviations which may exist such as that due to incorrect length of Flinders bar or even due to Coefficients A and E. The value of Coefficient A cannot be determined by means of the deflector as it does not contribute to directive force, whatever the heading. Coefficient E contributes to directive force only on the intercardinal points. It does not contribute at all to directive force if, as is almost invariably the case, only the cardinal points N, E, S and W are used.

The disadvantage, therefore, of the use of a deflector for compass correction lies not in the fact that residual deviations are almost sure to be present, but that their value and sign are unknown.

As previously stated, the errors when using the de Colongue deflector are minimised. A prism is fitted which presents the image of the pointer at the level of the card, and the line of sight is so arranged that parallax is avoided. The angle of deflection can only be 90°. The measurement is still subject to errors due to yaw, and to change of course after the base plate has been clamped.

The Theory of correction of the compass using Soft Iron Spheres. The duty of the soft iron corrector used is to make the effect of the rods a and e equal to satisfy the condition that there shall be no deviation, i.e. that $\bar{D} = 0$.

On page 74 we see that $D = \dfrac{a - e}{2\lambda}$ $\therefore$ if $a = e$ then $D = 0$.

Any lump of iron which is symmetrical about a vertical athwartship plane passing through the pivot of the ship's compass and which lies wholly on one side of the pivot will perform the above requirement.

By virtue of its shape it must produce the effects of $+e$, $-a$ and $-k$ rods, the degree to which these rods are present depends upon the shape of the lump and its distance from the compass.

The essential point is that by virtue of its symmetry no d rod effect can be present nor if two lumps are used which are an exact pair and are equally distant from the compass can any effect of f rod or h rod be present.

Many such devices have been used such as $+e$ bars of some German binnacles and $-a$ bars of some Italian equipments. The Japanese use $+e$ and $-a$ plates and even similar boxes containing lengths of chain have been used by the Dutch and used to be found at the steering compasses of British sailing ships.

The soft iron spheres used on British binnacles are preferred for the following reasons:

(1) They are a smooth convenient shape which obstructs the bridge less than many other shapes.

(2) The demagnetising effect of their shape renders them particularly unlikely to acquire or retain any remanent permanent

magnetism although, as previously stated, provision is made to allow for this by arranging that they always fit in their brackets with the same orientation with respect to the fore and aft line. This allows any permanent field they might have to be corrected with P, Q and R.

(3) The weak compass magnet needles used ensure that the correctors function almost entirely as if the compass was absent. This is not quite true but the effect is not sufficiently serious for it to be strictly necessary to move the spheres when the ship moves to a location where H varies considerably from that in which the last swing for adjustment took place.

(4) The simplicity of the theory of the behaviour of ideal spherical correctors used under ideal conditions is a good point in their favour.

In the following investigations use is made of the following proposition which has already been discussed on page 31, and it may be stated thus:

Let P be a unit red pole distant R from the centre O of a magnet of moment M the direction of P being at an angle θ to clockwise of the positive direction of the axis of the magnet, $i.e.$ the direction from its South to North Pole. ($Fig.$ 68).

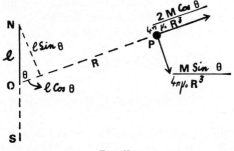

FIG. 68

The forces acting upon a unit red pole at P due to the magnet are

(i) A force $\dfrac{2M \cos \theta}{4\pi\mu_0 R^3}$ in the direction OP.

and (ii) A force $\dfrac{M \sin \theta}{4\pi\mu_0 R^3}$ in a direction 90° clockwise from OP.

In $Fig.$ 69 consider a single sphere placed with centre S, distant R from the compass centre C in a direction to starboard of the ship's head by the angle ϕ. It can be assumed that the magnetism induced in the sphere by a uniform field H will be that of a doublet of moment pH with its centre at S and its axis in the direction of the field H. p is a constant equal to $\dfrac{r^3}{4\pi\mu_0}$ where r is the radius of the sphere. In this connection a hollow sphere of which the thickness of the shell is of the order of one-tenth of the diameter may be considered to act in the same manner as a solid sphere of the same diameter.

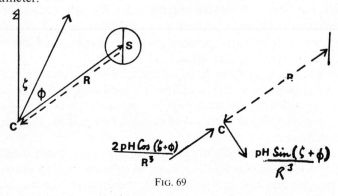

FIG. 69

Effect of the earth's induction. The sphere, when magnetised by the horizontal component of the earth's field, acts as a dipole of moment pH directed towards magnetic North.

The forces at the compass due to this dipole are:

$$\frac{2pH \cos (\zeta + \phi)}{R^3} \text{ in the direction } CS$$

and $\quad \dfrac{pH \sin (\zeta + \phi)}{R^3}$ in the direction 90° clockwise of CS

Using the same arguments as those used in Chapter XI, page 71, the components of these two forces towards Magnetic East are:

$$\frac{2pH \cos}{R^3}(\zeta + \phi) \sin (\zeta + \phi)$$

and $\quad \dfrac{pH \sin}{R^3}(\zeta + \phi) \cos (\zeta + \phi)$

These give a total force to Magnetic East or

$$\frac{2pH \cos}{R^3}(\zeta + \phi) \sin (\zeta + \phi) + \frac{pH \sin}{R^3}(\zeta + \phi) \cos (\zeta + \phi)$$

$$= \frac{3pH \sin}{R^3}(\zeta + \phi) \cos (\zeta + \phi)$$

$$= \frac{3pH\,2\sin}{2R^3}(\zeta + \phi)\cos(\zeta + \phi)$$

$$= \frac{3pH\,2\sin}{2R^3}(\zeta + \phi) \qquad \text{(See (9), page 18)}$$

$$= \frac{3pH\,\sin}{2R^3}(2\zeta + 2\phi)$$

$$= 3pH\,(\sin 2\zeta \cos 2\phi + \cos 2\zeta \sin 2\phi) \qquad \text{(See (1), page 18)}$$

$$= \left\{\frac{3pH}{2R^3}\cos 2\phi\right\}\sin 2\zeta + \left\{\frac{3pH}{2R^3}\sin 2\phi\right\}\cos 2\zeta$$

The components of the two forces in the direction Magnetic North are:

$$\frac{2pH}{R^3}\cos(\zeta + \phi)\cos(\zeta + \phi)$$

and $\quad \dfrac{-pH}{R^3}\sin(\zeta + \phi)\sin(\zeta + \phi)\quad$ (pH is negative in the direction anti-clockwise of CS)

The force to Magnetic North is therefore

$$\frac{2pH}{R^3}\cos^2(\zeta + \phi) - \frac{pH}{R^3}\sin^2(\zeta + \phi)$$

Referring again to page 18 (10) *et seq.* we can rewrite the above equation as

$$\frac{2pH}{R^3}\{\tfrac{1}{2} + \tfrac{1}{2}\cos 2(\zeta + \phi)\} - \frac{pH}{R^3}\{\tfrac{1}{2} - \tfrac{1}{2}\cos 2(\zeta + \phi)\}$$

$$= \frac{pH}{R^3} + \frac{pH}{R^3}\cos 2(\zeta + \phi) - \frac{pH}{2R^3} + \frac{pH}{2R^3}\cos 2(\zeta + \phi)$$

$$= \frac{pH}{2R^3} + \frac{3pH}{2R^3}\cos 2(\zeta + \phi)$$

$$= \frac{pH}{2R^3} + \frac{3pH}{2R^3}\cos (2\zeta + 2\phi)$$

$$= \frac{pH}{2R^3} + \frac{3pH}{2R^3}(\cos 2\zeta \cos 2\phi - \sin 2\zeta \sin 2\phi)$$

$$= \frac{pH}{2R^3} + \frac{3pH}{2R^3}(\cos 2\zeta \cos 2\phi) - \frac{3pH}{2R^3}(\sin 2\zeta \sin 2\phi)$$

Thus the *total* force to North is

$$H + \frac{pH}{2R^3} + \left\{\frac{3pH}{2R^3}\cos 2\phi\right\}\cos 2\zeta - \left\{\frac{3pH}{2R^3}\sin 2\phi\right\}\sin 2\zeta$$

Now referring to the total force to Magnetic East and to Magnetic North on page 71 and to equations (6′) and (7′) and to the consequential equation (10) on page 74, we see that we can write:

$$\tan \delta \frac{\left\{\dfrac{3p}{2R^3} \cos 2\phi\right\} \sin 2\zeta + \left\{\dfrac{3p}{2R^3} \sin 2\phi\right\} \cos 2\zeta}{1 + \dfrac{p}{2R^3} - \left\{\dfrac{3p}{2R^3} \sin 2\phi\right\} \sin 2\zeta + \left\{\dfrac{3p}{2R^3} \cos 2\phi\right\} \cos 2\zeta}$$

From which

$$\lambda_s = 1 + \frac{p}{2R^3}$$

$$\bar{D}_s = \frac{1}{\lambda_s} \frac{3p}{2R^3} \cos 2\phi$$

$$\bar{E}_s = \frac{1}{\lambda_s} \frac{3p}{2R^3} \sin 2\phi$$

Effect of induction in the spheres by the compass needles. Consider a single sphere centre S at an angle ϕ from the ship's head at distance R from C the centre of the magnetic needle system. (*Fig. 70*).

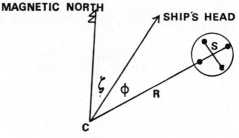

FIG. 70

The forces due to the needles of moment m at S are

$$\frac{2m}{R^3} \cos (\zeta + \phi) \text{ in the direction } CS$$

and $\dfrac{m}{R^3} \sin (\zeta + \phi)$ in the direction 90° clockwise of CS.

The spheres are magnetised by these forces and give equivalent dipoles of moment:

$$\frac{2pm}{R^3} \cos (\zeta + \phi) \text{ in the direction } CS$$

and $\dfrac{pm}{R^3} \sin(\zeta + \phi)$ in the direction 90° clockwise of CS.

The dipoles give forces at the compass of

$$\frac{4pm}{R^6} \cos(\zeta + \phi) \text{ in the direction } CS$$

and $\dfrac{pm}{R^6} \sin(\zeta + \phi)$ in the direction 90° to anti-clockwise of CS

The Easterly components of these forces are:

$$4pm \cos(\zeta + \phi) \sin(\zeta + \phi)$$

and $-\dfrac{pm}{R^6} \sin(\zeta + \phi) \cos(\zeta + \phi)$

These may be written

$$\frac{4pm}{2R^6} 2 \sin(\zeta + \phi) \cos(\zeta + \phi) - \frac{pm}{2R^6} 2 \sin(\zeta + \phi) \cos(\zeta + \phi)$$

$$= \frac{3pm}{2R^6} \sin 2(\zeta + \phi) \qquad\qquad \text{(See (9), page 18).}$$

$$= \frac{3pm}{2R^6} \sin(2\zeta + 2\phi)$$

$$= \frac{3pm}{2R^6} (\sin 2\zeta \cos 2\phi + \cos 2\zeta \sin 2\phi)$$

$$= \left\{\frac{3pm}{2R^6} \cos 2\phi\right\} \sin 2\zeta + \left\{\frac{3pm}{2R^6} \sin 2\phi\right\} \cos 2\zeta$$

The Northerly components of the forces are:

$$\frac{4pm}{R^6} \cos(\zeta + \phi) \cos(\zeta + \phi) = \frac{4pm}{R^6} \cos^2(\zeta + \phi)$$

and $\dfrac{pm}{R^6} \sin(\zeta + \phi) \sin(\zeta + \phi) = \dfrac{pm}{R^6} \sin^2(\zeta + \phi)$

which may be written

$$\frac{4pm}{R^6} \cos^2(\zeta + \phi) + \frac{pm}{R^6} \sin^2(\zeta + \phi)$$

$$= \frac{3pm}{R^6} \cos^2(\zeta + \phi) + \frac{pm}{R^6} \cos^2(\zeta + \phi) + \frac{pm}{R^6} \sin^2(\zeta + \phi)$$

F:

$$= \frac{3pm}{R^6} \cos^2 (\zeta + \phi) + \frac{pm}{R^6} \left(\sin^2 (\zeta + \phi) + \cos^2 (\zeta + \phi) \right)$$

$$= \frac{pm}{R^6} + \frac{3pm}{R^6} \cos^2 (\zeta + \phi)$$

$$= \frac{pm}{R^6} + \frac{3pm}{2R^6} \cos^2 (\zeta + \phi) + \frac{3pm}{2R^6} \left(1 - \sin^2 (\zeta + \phi) \right)$$

$$= \frac{pm}{R^6} + \frac{3pm}{2R^6} \cos^2 (\zeta + \phi) + \frac{3pm}{2R^6} - \frac{3pm}{2R^6} \sin^2 (\zeta + \phi)$$

$$= \frac{pm}{R^6} + \frac{3pm}{2R^6} + \frac{3pm}{2R^6} \left(\cos^2 (\zeta + \phi) - \sin^2 (\zeta + \phi) \right)$$

$$= \frac{5pm}{2R^6} + \frac{3pm}{2R^6} \cos 2(\zeta + \phi)$$

The total force to North, including H, is therefore

$$H + \frac{5pm}{2R^6} + \frac{3pm}{2R^6} \cos 2(\zeta + \phi)$$

$$= H \left\{ 1 + \frac{5pm}{2HR^6} + \left(\frac{3pm}{2HR^6} \cos 2\phi \right) \cos 2\zeta - \left(\frac{3pm}{2HR^6} \sin 2\phi \right) \sin 2\zeta \right\}$$

Referring again to equations (6) and (7), page 71, and to equation (10), page 74, it follows that

$$\tan \text{dev} = \frac{\left(\dfrac{3pm}{2HR^6} \cos 2\phi \right) \sin 2\zeta + \left(\dfrac{3pm}{2HR^6} \sin 2\phi \right) \cos 2\zeta}{1 + \dfrac{5pm}{2HR^6} + \left(\dfrac{3pm}{2HR^6} \cos 2\phi \right) \cos 2\zeta - \left(\dfrac{3pm}{2HR^6} \sin 2\phi \right) \sin 2\zeta}$$

So that
$$\lambda m = 1 + \frac{5pm}{2HR^6}$$

$$\bar{D}m = \frac{1}{\lambda} \times \frac{3pm}{2HR^6} \cos 2\phi$$

$$\bar{E}m = \frac{1}{\lambda} \times \frac{3pm}{2HR^6} \sin 2\phi$$

From the above theory it will be seen that if $\bar{D}$ to be corrected is positive and if $\bar{E}$ to be corrected is zero then $\cos 2\phi$ must equal -1 and $\sin 2\phi$ equals 0.

Hence
$$2\phi = 180° \quad \text{and} \quad \phi = 90°$$

If $\bar{E}$ to be corrected is positive then $\sin 2\phi$ must be negative. Thus for correcting a positive $\bar{D}$ and a positive $\bar{E}$ we require 2ϕ to be an angle such that its cosine is negative and its sine negative. The angle must lie, therefore between $180°$ and $270°$.

$$\frac{\bar{E}}{\bar{D}} = \tan 2\phi \text{ where } 2\phi = (180° + \theta) \text{ and } \theta \text{ is less than } 90°$$

Tan θ is numerically equal to $\dfrac{\bar{E}}{\bar{D}}$ \qquad\qquad (See *Fig.* 8, page 13).

Hence \qquad $\tan 2\phi = \dfrac{\bar{E}}{\bar{D}}$ \quad and \quad $\phi = 90° + \tfrac{1}{2}\tan^{-1}\dfrac{\bar{E}}{\bar{D}}$

Similarly when $\bar{D}$ to be corrected is positive and $\bar{E}$ to be corrected is negative then 2ϕ must be an angle whose cosine is negative but whose sine is positive, it lies, therefore, between $90°$ and $180°$.

Thus for correcting a positive D and a negative E

$$\tan 2\phi = \frac{\bar{E}}{\bar{D}} \quad \text{and} \quad \phi = 90° - \tfrac{1}{2}\tan\frac{\bar{E}}{\bar{D}}$$

Referring to page 81, we can write

$$\bar{D} \text{ in radians} = D° \times \frac{\pi}{180}$$

$$\bar{E} \text{ in radians} = E° \times \frac{\pi}{180}$$

Then \qquad $\dfrac{\bar{E}}{\bar{D}} = \dfrac{E° \times \dfrac{\pi}{180}}{D° \times \dfrac{\pi}{180}} = \dfrac{E°}{D°}$

Therefore for correcting $+D°$ only, (with $E°$ nothing $\phi = 90°$) and the spheres must be placed athwartships.

For correcting $+D°$ and $+E°$

$$\phi = 90° + \tfrac{1}{2}\tan^{-1}\frac{E}{D}$$

and the spheres must be slewed clockwise to angle from thwartships which is half the angle of which $\dfrac{E}{D}$ is the tangent and where $\dfrac{E}{D}$ is the ratio of the numerical values of E° and D° regardless of their sign.

For correcting $+D^\circ$ and $-E^\circ$

$$\phi = 90^\circ - \tfrac{1}{2} \tan^{-1} \frac{E}{D}$$

and the spheres must be slewed anti-clockwise from thwartships to an angle which is half the angle of which $\dfrac{E}{D}$ is the tangent.

It may be noted that a Flinders bar acts like a small sphere. All the arguments referred to above apply to the D effects due to the bar, but in practice the effect is slightly to increase the positive D of the ship and is counteracted by the spheres.

Finally it follows that the order of mechanical correction given in the next chapter should be adhered to.

CHAPTER XVII

THE MECHANICAL CORRECTION OF THE COMPASS

IT will be realised from the theoretical considerations discussed in the foregoing chapters that certain precautions must be taken if the compass is to give satisfactory results. These may be enumerated under the following headings.

The position of the compass. In merchant ships the placing of the standard compass does not always receive all the consideration it deserves, but the following rules should, as far as possible, be adhered to:

(1) The standard compass should be placed so as to obtain a clear view of as much of the horizon as possible.

(2) It should be in the centre line of the ship and as far away as possible from large masses of magnetic material, especially those giving vertical effects, and from movable iron.

(3) No magnetic material should be in any direction nearer than 10 feet (3 m) from the standard compass or 6 feet (2 m) from a steering compass.

(4) No electrical or electro-magnetic instruments should be near enough to any compass to have any effect on it.

(5) All electric leads in the vicinity of the compass should be run so that the supply and return leads of the same circuit are clipped together with non-magnetic clips, and secured in position by non-magnetic fastenings.

Note. The Admiralty Compass Department publish a pamphlet giving the "safe distances" for most instruments and apparatus fitted in ships. The Ministry of Transport also lay down "safe" and "conceded" distances for certain equipment. The "safe" distances should be used whenever possible.

The ship should be swung for deviations of the compass, which may require adjustment:

(1) After the ship has suffered any severe impact such as collision.

(2) After being struck by lightning.

(3) After any major structural alteration or major repairs.

(4) After loading or discharging by means of electro-magnets.

(5) After lying in one direction for a long period of time.

(6) If any of the correctors have been moved for reasons other than adjustment.

(7) At least once a year.

Note. The carriage of cargoes containing magnetic material may affect deviations during the voyage.

Precautions before swinging for deviations and/or adjustment:

(1) The ship should be upright.

(2) The funnels should be at their sea-going temperature.

(3) All movable iron should be in its sea-going position.

(4) No other ship should be within 3 cables of the ship during the swing.

(5) The azimuth mirror should be tested and, if necessary, adjusted.

(6) The lubber point may require checking to make certain it is in the fore and aft vertical plane through the pivot.

(7) The compass card should be tested for friction by deflecting the north point about 2° to the right by means of a magnet and then about 2° to the left. If the card returns to its previous position of rest, as indicated by the direction of the ship's head, after each deflection there is no friction.

Precautions when adjusting:

(1) The permanent magnets must not be placed within a distance of twice their length from the compass needles, or within a distance of six times the length of the longest compass needles, which ever is the greater.

(2) The vertical fore and aft plane passing through the centre of the compass needle system must pass through the centre of all athwartship magnets, the centre of the vertical magnet system (heeling error magnets), and the longitudinal axis of the Flinders bar.

(3) The vertical athwartship plane passing through the centre of the compass needle system must pass through the centre of all fore and aft magnets, the centre of the vertical magnet system, and the centre of the spheres.

(4) The horizontal plane passing through the centre of the compass needle system must pass through the centre of the spheres and a point on the Flinders bar one-twelfth (1/12) of its length from the upper end.

Note. The distance of the spheres from the compass needle system must be such that Coefficient D (and E if necessary) is corrected. Induction in the spheres by the needles is reduced to a minimum if the needles of the system are short compared with the distance of the centre of the system from the centre of the spheres.

This is normally the case in the better types of modern compass cards.

It must also be borne in mind that the proper system of needles is such that the like poles of symmetrical pairs subtend an angle of 60° at the centre, or sextantal deviations may be present.

Order of Correction:

(1) The spheres should be placed to correct for Coefficient D (and for E if necessary). If the value of the deviation it is required to correct is known, the distance of the spheres from the compass may be found from Tables. If not, place the spheres half-way along the brackets. The spheres should be suitably marked to ensure that in the event of any further adjustment they are not turned in azimuth, so that they may retain the same orientation with respect to the fore and aft line of the ship.

An approximate value for D could be found by observing the deviations on the four quadrantal points; this necessitates an additional swing. If the spheres are already in place, by consulting the records of deviations, it may be ascertained if material alteration in their position is required.

(2) The Flinders bar is then placed if not already in position. If the ship is new, the position and amount known to be fitted in a similar type ship should be used. If this is not known, 12 inches (30·5 cm) of Flinders bar may be placed on the side of the binnacle toward the nearer end of the ship; this assumes that the compass is forward of and above the centre of the ship's superstructure and hull.

As the Flinders bar acts as a small sphere giving a small $+a$ rod and a small $-e$ rod effect, this may necessitate the spheres being moved in about half an inch.

The Flinders bar must be slewed if necessary to correct for any f rod effect, if present.

(3) The heeling error should now be corrected with the aid of the Heeling Error or Vertical Force Instrument as described on page 100 *et seq.*

The ship's head should be placed in an easterly or westerly direction if there is likelihood of any g rod effect, otherwise the direction of the ship's head is immaterial. In choosing a place ashore free from local interference, the instrument should be kept at least three feet from the ground.

(4) The horizontal permanent magnets are next placed for the correction of Coefficients B and C. The coefficient having the greater value should be attended to first.

(*a*) Coefficient *B* is usually the greater, in which case the ship's head should be placed East or West by compass and fore and aft magnets inserted until there is no deviation showing.

(*b*) Then place the ship's head North or South by compass and correct Coefficient *C* by inserting athwartship permanent magnets until there is no deviation showing.

(*c*) If there was a large deviation on North or South, which ever was used, go back to the *same* heading used for (*a*) and readjust the fore and aft magnets. This is done because a large uncorrected Coefficient *C* would be affecting the directive force at the compass position when *B* was first corrected.

(*d*) Next place the ship on the *opposite* heading to (*a*) and halve any deviation showing by re-adjusting the fore and aft magnets.

(*e*) Now place the ship on the *opposite* heading to that used in (*b*), halving the remaining deviation by re-adjusting the athwartship magnets.

(*f*) Then place the ship's head on the quadrantal point between the headings used in (*d*) and (*e*) and make any necessary final adjustment to the position of the spheres.

(*g*) Finally, swing the ship and obtain the residual deviations on at least eight, but preferably sixteen, equidistant points. This operation should take at least 40 minutes, and the ship should be steadied on each point; this admits also a more accurate comparison with the steering compass being made.

(*h*) If required, λ_2 may now be found as described on page 121 . *et seq.*

Note. If bearings of a distant object are used to obtain the deviations, the effect of parallax must be borne in mind. The parallax in a 100 metre radius of swing at six miles distance is about half a degree.

If a shore compass is used to obtain reciprocal bearings, an efficient means of signalling must be arranged.

If bearings of a heavenly body are used, it is more convenient to work out and tabulate the magnetic bearings beforehand covering the period of time of the swing.

When the bearings of two or more known terrestrial objects in line are used, and the deviations obtained from transits, no particular precautions are required.

If a gyro compass is used it must be ascertained that it has no error, but one or other of the methods mentioned above is preferable.

The deviations of the steering or the after compass are obtained from comparison with the standard compass.

It is possible, after a vessel has been struck by lightning, for its compass to become *frozen*, that is to say, the North point of its card will point in a certain direction with reference to the fore and aft line of the ship irrespective of the direction in which the ship is heading. This would indicate that an extremely strong blue pole had developed in that part of the ship due to the electrical discharge.

Before any normal compensation can be made the compass must be *freed* by inserting fore and aft and/or athwartship magnets in the binnacle in such a way that the compass will again respond to alterations of course. For instance, assume that the North point of the card tended to point two points on the port bow for all headings of the ship—place the ship heading about SSW so that the North point of the card is pointing approximately South, then insert fore and aft magnets, red ends forward, and athwartship magnets, red ends to port, until the card is able to approximately reverse its direction. In this particular case the fore and aft component should obviously be the stronger of the two.

A similar state might be found at the steering compass position of a ship due to bad siting, for instance the binnacle having been placed too close to a bulkhead. The compass must then be freed as described above before the ordinary correction of the compass is carried out. It is to be hoped, however, that such a condition will seldom be found in ships of the present day.

APPENDIX

WORKED EXAMPLES

(1) A horizontal vibrating needle made 10 complete vibrations in 94 seconds in the earth's field. On board a ship at the compass position the time of 10 complete vibrations was as follows: on North, $88\frac{1}{2}$ seconds; on East, 95 seconds; on South, 104 seconds; on West, 121 seconds, the ship's head being magnetic in each case. Neglecting any deviation present, find the approximate value of λ and the values of the approximate Coefficients B, C and D in terms of the deviation to the nearest degree.

Answer. $\quad T_H = \quad 9.4 \qquad T_H^2 = 88.4$

$$T_N = \quad 8.85 \quad T_N^2 = 78.3 \quad \frac{1}{T_N^2} = 0.0128$$

$$T_S = 10.4 \quad T_S^2 = 108.2 \quad \frac{1}{T_S^2} = 0.0093$$

$$T_E = \quad 9.5 \quad T_E^2 = \quad 90.3 \quad \frac{1}{T_E^2} = 0.0111$$

$$T_W = 12.1 \quad T_W^2 = 146.4 \quad \frac{1}{T_W^2} = 0.0068$$

$$\lambda = \frac{T_H^2}{\frac{1}{4}(T_N^2 + T_S^2 + T_E^2 + T_W^2)}$$

$$= \frac{88.4}{105.8} = 0.834.$$

To find the constant k of the instrument

$$k = \frac{4}{\dfrac{1}{T_N^2} + \dfrac{1}{T_S^2} + \dfrac{1}{T_E^2} + \dfrac{1}{T_W^2}} = \frac{4}{0.04}$$

$$= 100$$

$$\text{Sin } B° = \frac{k}{2}\left(\frac{1}{T_N^2} - \frac{1}{T_S^2}\right) = 50\,(0.0128 - 0.0093)$$

$$= 0.175$$

$$B = +10°$$

$$\text{Sin } C^\circ = \frac{k}{2}\left(\frac{1}{T_W^2} - \frac{1}{T_E^2}\right) = 50(0\!\cdot\!0068 - 0\!\cdot\!0111)$$

$$= -0\!\cdot\!215$$

$$C = -12\tfrac{1}{2}^\circ$$

$$\text{Sin } D^\circ = \frac{k}{4}\left[\left(\frac{1}{T_N^2} + \frac{1}{T_S^2}\right) - \left(\frac{1}{T_E^2} + \frac{1}{T_W^2}\right)\right]$$

$$= 25(0\!\cdot\!0221 - 0\!\cdot\!0179)$$

$$= 0\!\cdot\!105$$

$$D = +6^\circ.$$

(2) From the following table of deviations found on eight equidistant points by compass, evaluate (a) the approximate coefficients, and (b) the exact coefficients.

Ship's head	Deviation	Ship's head	Deviation
North	6° E	South	10° W
NE	5¼° E	SW	2¾° E
East	4° W	West	8° E
SE	13¼° W	NW	5¾° E

Answer

Hd.	Dev.	Sin	Prod.	Cos	Prod.	Sin 2	Prod.	Cos 2	Prod.
N	+6	0	0	1	+6	0	0	1	+6
NE	+5¼	·707	+3·7	·707	+3·7	1	+5¼	0	0
E	−4	1	−4	0	0	0	0	−1	+4
SE	−13¼	·707	−9·4	−·707	+9·4	−1	+13¼	0	0
S	−10	0	0	−1	+10·0	0	0	1	−10
SW	+2¾	−·707	−1·9	−·707	−1·9	1	+2¾	0	0
W	+8	−1	−8	0	0	0	0	−1	−8
NW	+5¾	−·707	−4	·707	+4	−1	−5¾	0	0

$$8A = +\tfrac{1}{2} \qquad 4B = -23\!\cdot\!6 \qquad 4C = +31\!\cdot\!2 \qquad 4D = +15\tfrac{1}{2} \qquad 4E = -8$$
$$A = 0 \qquad B = -5\!\cdot\!9 \qquad C = +7\!\cdot\!8 \qquad D = +3\!\cdot\!9 \qquad E = -2$$

Or approximately

B is the mean of deviations on East and West with the sign on West reversed

$$= \frac{-4 - 8}{2} = -6^\circ.$$

C is the mean of the deviations on North and South with the sign on South reversed

$$= \frac{6 + 10}{2} = +8^\circ.$$

D is the mean of the deviations on the quadrantal points with the sign on SE and NW reversed

$$= \frac{5\frac{1}{4} + 13\frac{1}{4} + 2\frac{3}{4} - 5\frac{3}{4}}{4} = 3 \cdot 9°.$$

E is the mean of the deviations on the cardinal points with the sign on East and West reversed

$$= \frac{6 + 4 - 10 - 8}{4} = -2°.$$

The exact coefficients

$$\bar{A} = A = 0$$

$$\bar{B} = B + \frac{BD}{2} = \sin B \left(1 + \tfrac{1}{2} \sin D\right) = -0 \cdot 104 \left(1 + 0 \cdot 035\right)$$

$$= -0 \cdot 107$$

$$\bar{C} = C - \frac{CD}{2} = \sin C \left(1 - \tfrac{1}{2} \sin D\right) = \quad 0 \cdot 139 \left(1 - 0 \cdot 035\right)$$

$$= +0 \cdot 134$$

$$\bar{D} = \sin D \quad = +0 \cdot 070$$

$$\bar{E} = \sin E \quad = -0 \cdot 035.$$

(3) Given that Coefficient B at Liverpool ($H = 18$, Dip $= 68°$) was $+4°$, and at Cape Town ($H = 17$, Dip $= -60°$) was found to be $+9 \cdot 5°$, state how the correctors should be placed in order to compensate for Coefficient B at Cape Town. (Neglect the value of λ.)

Answer. This problem may be solved in two ways depending on whether (*a*), the value of the deviation to be corrected by the Flinders bar is required, or (*b*), the *c*-rod value is required, in order to find the length of Flinders bar from Tables.

Method (*a*)—We require values at Cape Town, therefore:

Let x be the deviation caused by the permanent part of B at Cape Town.

Let y be the deviation caused by the induced part of B at Cape Town.

Then $\qquad\qquad x + y = 9 \cdot 5$ at Cape Town $\qquad\qquad$ (1)

and $\qquad \dfrac{17}{18}x + \dfrac{\tan 68}{-\tan 60}y = 4$ at Liverpool $\qquad\qquad$ (2)

$$0 \cdot 94x - 1 \cdot 43y = 4$$

$$0.94x + 0.94y = 8.93 \text{ (1 multiplied by } 0.94\text{)}$$
$$2.37y = 4.93 \text{ (by subtraction)}$$
$$y = 2.1$$
$$x = 9.5 - 2.1 = 7.4,$$

y being positive, indicating a red induced pole abaft the compass, a length of Flinders bar to correct $2.1°$ deviation is required on the fore side of the compass. (Flinders bar will have a red pole uppermost as the Dip is negative.) Fore and aft magnets, red ends forward, will be required to correct $7.4°$ deviation.

Method (b)

The equation $\quad P + cZ = \lambda H \sin B$

gives for Liverpool $\quad P + c \times 18 \tan 68 = 18 \sin 4$

and for Cape Town $\quad P + c \times 17 \times -\tan 60 = 17 \sin 9.5$

subtracting we get $\quad c(18 \tan 68 + 17 \tan 60)$
$$= 18 \sin 4 - 17 \sin 9.5$$
$$74c = -1.54$$
$$c = -0.021$$

From either equation $\quad P = +2.2$

From the appropriate Table the length of Flinders bar to correct a c value of 0.021 may be found.

To find the deviation to correct by permanent magnets at Cape Town

$$\text{Sin } \delta = \frac{2.2}{17} = 0.13$$

whence $\qquad \delta = +7\frac{1}{2}°$ as found by method (a).

If the deviation corresponding to the c-rod value at Cape Town is required

$$\text{Sin } \delta = -0.021 \times -\tan 60$$
$$= 0.036$$

whence $\qquad \delta = +2.1°$ as found by method (a).

(4) In the River Clyde ($H = 17$, $Z = 45$), Coefficient B was corrected by placing a length of Flinders bar on the fore side of the binnacle to correct an estimated $5°$ of deviation, and then fore and aft magnets, red ends forward, were placed to correct the remaining $13°$ of deviation. On arrival at Cape Town ($H = 17$,

$Z = -33$), a Coefficient $-B$, of $5°$, was found to be present with the correctors still in place. What adjustment should be made at Cape Town?

Answer.

Let x be the deviation due to permanent magnetism at Cape Town.

Let y be the deviation due to induced magnetism at Cape Town.

$$\text{At Cape Town} \qquad x + y = -5 \left.\right\rbrace \text{ with correctors}$$
$$\text{In the Clyde } \frac{17}{17}x + \frac{17}{-33} \times \frac{45}{17}y = \ \ 0 \ \left.\right\rbrace \text{ in place.}$$

$$x - 1{\cdot}364y = \ \ \ 0$$
$$\text{Subtracting} \qquad\qquad 2{\cdot}364y = \ -5$$
$$y = -2{\cdot}1$$
$$x = -2{\cdot}9.$$

Flinders bar at Cape Town will be causing

$$5 \times \frac{17}{45} \times \frac{-33}{17} = -3{\cdot}67.$$

Hence Flinders bar must be reduced in length to correct

$$3{\cdot}67 - 2{\cdot}1 = 1{\cdot}57 \text{ or say } 1\tfrac{1}{2}° \text{ of deviation.}$$

Magnets at Cape Town will be causing

$$-13 \times \frac{17}{17} = -13°$$

and must be reduced to correct $13 - 2{\cdot}9 = 10{\cdot}1$, say $10°$ of deviation.

(5) A vessel whose Flinders bar was accurately adjusted to correct $5°$ of induced $-B$, was found to have, after certain structural alterations, an induced C of $1°$. How should this be compensated for?

Answer. Flinders bar must be slewed to port to an angle with the fore and aft line of which $\dfrac{C}{B} = \dfrac{1}{5}$ is the tangent.

$$\text{Tan}^{-1} 0{\cdot}2 = 11\tfrac{1}{2}°.$$

Theoretically its length must also be increased to correct $\sqrt{5^2 + 1^2} = \sqrt{26} = 5{\cdot}1°$ deviation, in this case a negligible increase.

(6) After an analysis of deviations it was found that a vessel had

a coefficient $+D$, or $4°$, and a coefficient $+E$, of $2°$. How should these deviations be compensated for?

Answer. As D is positive, the spheres must be slewed to an angle with the athwartship plane through the compass such that the tangent of twice the angle is $\dfrac{E}{D}$.

$$\text{Angle of slew} = \tfrac{1}{2}\tan^{-1}\frac{2}{4} = 0\!\cdot\!5 = \frac{26\frac{1}{2}°}{2} = 13\tfrac{1}{4}°.$$

As E is positive, the port sphere must be moved forward and the starboard sphere moved aft.

The distance from the compass must be such that the spheres will correct a maximum deviation equal to

$$\sqrt{D^2 - E^2} = \sqrt{4^2 - 2^2} = \sqrt{20} = 4\tfrac{1}{2}°,$$

for which the corresponding distance may be taken from the appropriate Tables if available.

(7) From the following deflector readings evaluate the coefficients. State the settings at which corrections should be made and the directions in which the correctors should be placed. If the reading with the compass ashore, free from local disturbance, was 14·7, calculate the value of λ. Assume any deviation present to be negligible and that the Flinders bar is in place.

Ship's head	Reading	Ship's head	Reading
North	15·55	South	11·2
NE	16·5	SW	9·8
East	14·2	West	9·0
SE	11·56	NW	12·15

Answer. To find k, the constant for the instrument,

$$k = \frac{4}{R_N + R_S + R_E + R_W} = \frac{4}{49\cdot95} = 0\!\cdot\!08$$

$$\text{Sin } B° = \frac{k}{2}(R_N - R_S) = 0\!\cdot\!04(15\!\cdot\!55 - 11\!\cdot\!2)$$

$$= 0\!\cdot\!174 \quad \text{and} \quad B = +10°$$

$$\text{Sin } C° = \frac{k}{2}(R_W - R_E) = 0\!\cdot\!04(9\!\cdot\!0 - 14\!\cdot\!2)$$

$$= -0\!\cdot\!208 \quad \text{and} \quad C = -12°$$

$$\text{Sin } D° = \frac{k}{4}(R_N + R_S) - (R_E + R_W) = 0\!\cdot\!02(26\!\cdot\!75 - 23\!\cdot\!2)$$

$$= 0\!\cdot\!071 \quad \text{and} \quad D = +4°$$

$$\text{Sin } E^\circ = \frac{k}{4}(R_{SE} + R_{NW}) - (R_{NE} + R_{SW}) = 0{\cdot}02(23{\cdot}71 - 26{\cdot}3)$$

$$= -0{\cdot}0518 \quad and \quad E = -3^\circ.$$

Setting for $B = \dfrac{R_N + R_S}{2} = \dfrac{26{\cdot}75}{2} = 13{\cdot}375.$

Fore and aft magnets, red ends forward, ship heading North or South. (Reading on North is greater than on South.)

Setting for $C = \dfrac{R_E + R_W}{2} = \dfrac{23{\cdot}2}{2} = 11{\cdot}6.$

Athwartship magnets, red ends to starboard, ship heading East or West. (Reading on East greater than on West.)

Setting for $D = \dfrac{1}{2}\left[\left(\dfrac{R_N + R_S}{2}\right) + \left(\dfrac{R_E + R_W}{2}\right)\right] = \dfrac{13{\cdot}375 + 11{\cdot}6}{2}$

$$= 12{\cdot}487.$$

Spheres must be placed athwartships and slewed to half the angle of which the tangent is $\dfrac{E}{D} = \dfrac{3}{4}$, *i.e.*, $18\frac{1}{2}^\circ$ from the athwartship plane. Set instrument to 12·487 and with ship's head East or West move spheres in until the full deflection is obtained. (Port sphere is slewed aft, and starboard sphere forward.)

To compute λ

$$\lambda = \frac{1}{4}\frac{R_N + R_E + R_S + R_W}{R_A} \quad \text{where } R_A \text{ is the shore reading}$$

$$= \frac{1}{4}\left(\frac{49{\cdot}95}{14{\cdot}7}\right) = 0{\cdot}85.$$

(8) A heavy derrick stepped amidships is topped up to an angle of 60° with the horizontal and guyed fore and aft with its head forward of, and in the same horizontal plane as, the standard compass. In this position it causes a deviation of $4\frac{1}{2}^\circ$ East when the ship is heading East by compass at a place where $H = 20$ and $Z = 10$. Under the same conditions it causes $15\frac{1}{2}^\circ$ Easterly deviation when heading East at a place where $H = 12$ and $Z = 30$. Estimate the deviation it will cause when heading N 45° E at the latter place.

Answer. The deviations may be caused by permanent and/or induced magnetism. It is immaterial whether the permanent magnetism is considered horizontal or vertical. The induced part, if present, will consist of two effects, that due to a $+c$ rod and that due to a $+a$ rod.

For the same induction, $a = c \tan 30° = 0.577c$.

But a is induced by H, and c by Z, therefore at the second place

$$a = c \cot \theta = c\frac{12}{30} = 0\text{·}4c.$$

Again the effect of a will vary as $\sin \zeta'$ but the induction in the rod will vary as $\cos \zeta'$. Thus the effect on N 45° E $= a \sin 45 \cos 45 = 0\text{·}5a$.

Summing these effects we get

$$a = c \times 0\text{·}577 \times 0\text{·}4$$

and Coefficient $D = c \times 0\text{·}577 \times 0\text{·}4 \times 0\text{·}5 = 0\text{·}115c$.

The c rod effect is an induced Coefficient B and the permanent effect is a permanent Coefficient B.

The D effect is zero on East.

To "split" Coefficient B:

Let x be the deviation due to the permanent part at the second place.

Let y be the deviation due to the induced part at the second place.

Then at second place $x + y = 15\text{·}5$

and at first place $\dfrac{12}{20}x + \dfrac{12}{30} \times \dfrac{10}{20}y = 4\text{·}5$

$$0\text{·}6x + 0\text{·}2y = 4\text{·}5$$
$$0\text{·}6x + 0\text{·}6y = 9\text{·}3$$
$$0\text{·}4y = 4\text{·}8.$$

Deviation due to c rod $y = +12°$.

Coefficient $D = 0\text{·}115c = 0\text{·}115 \times 12 = +1\text{·}38°$.

Then deviation on N 45° E $= B \sin 45 + D \sin 90$

$$= 15\text{·}5 \times 0\text{·}707 + 1\text{·}38$$
$$= 10\text{·}96 + 1\text{·}38$$
$$= 12\text{·}34 \text{ or } 12\tfrac{1}{3}° \text{ E.}$$

(9) When a vessel is heeled 6° to starboard heading N 22° W the heeling error is found to be 5° W. What will the heeling error be when heeled 9° to port heading S 40° W?

Answer. Heeling error varies directly as the angle of heel and as the cosine of the course. Heel to starboard is positive and to port negative.

$$\text{H.E. on S } 40° \text{ W} = -5 \times \frac{-9}{6} \times \frac{\cos 220}{\cos 338}$$

$$= 7·5 \times \frac{-\cos 40}{+\cos 22}$$

$$= 7·5 \times \frac{-0·766}{+0·927}$$

$$= 7·5 \times -0·826$$

$$= -6·2 \text{ or } 6\tfrac{1}{4}° \text{ W.}$$

(10) A vessel has her heeling error compensated for while in the River Thames ($H = 18$, $Z = 42$). On arriving at the Magnetic Equator ($H = 36$) the heeling error was found to be 3° W when heading N 25° E and heeled 6° to starboard. This error was removed by adjusting the heeling-error bucket in the binnacle. What heeling error, if any, might be anticipated when heeled 10° to starboard and heading South off Newcastle, N.S.W. ($H = 24$, $Z = 54$)?

Answer. The heeling error consists of two parts, $(e - k) \tan \theta$ due to induction in soft iron and $\dfrac{R}{H}$ due to permanent magnetism. Both parts vary directly as the angle of heel and as the cosine of the course.

Newcastle, N.S.W., is in the Southern Hemisphere and therefore Z is negative.

Let x be the heeling error due to permanent magnetism in the Thames when heeled 6° to starboard heading N 25° E.

Let y be the heeling error due to induced magnetism in the Thames when heeled 6° to starboard heading N 25° E.

Then for Thames $x + y = 0$ ⎫ with corrector

and for Equator $\dfrac{x18}{36} + 0 = -3$ ⎬ magnets in place

whence $x = -6$

and $y = +6.$

After adjustment at the Equator the induced part is no longer compensated for, but the permanent part is accurately corrected.

Therefore the heeling error when heading South, heeled 10° to starboard, off Newcastle, N.S.W.

$$= 6 \times \frac{+10}{+6} \times \frac{18}{42} \times \frac{-54}{24} \times \frac{\cos 180}{\cos 25}$$

$$= 10 \times \frac{-27}{28} \times \frac{-1 \cdot 0}{0 \cdot 906}$$

$$= \frac{270}{25 \cdot 34}$$

$$= +10 \cdot 6 \text{ or } 10\frac{1}{2}° \text{ E}.$$

(11) A vessel 220 metres long has no deviation on any heading when upright on even keel. Later when heading 020° C and heeled 7° to port a deviation of 5° E is observed. What deviation may be anticipated when heading 230° by compass, heeled 4° to starboard and trimmed 6 metres by the stern?

Answer. Pitching error due to trim and heeling error may be treated as synonymous except that pitching error varies as the Sine of the Course and Heeling error varies as the Cosine of the Course.

The angle of pitch for 6 m trim toward the stem is positive and equals $\tan^{-1}$ or $\sin^{-1} \dfrac{6}{220} = 1\frac{1}{2}°$ say.

The same coefficient J causes both heeling and pitching errors.

Heeling error $= J.i. \cos \zeta'$

$$= J. - 7 \cos 020°$$

$$J = \frac{-5}{7} \sec 020°.$$

Hence for new course, heel and trim:

Heeling error $= \dfrac{-5}{7} \sec 020° \times 4 \times \cos 230°$

$$= +1 \cdot 95°.$$

Pitching error $= \dfrac{-5}{7} \sec 020° \times -1\frac{1}{2}° \times \sin 230°$

$$= -0 \cdot 86°.$$

Deviation due to list and trim $= +1 \cdot 95° - 0 \cdot 86°$
$$= +1 \cdot 09° \text{ or } 1 \cdot 1° \text{ E}.$$

(12) The compass of a certain ship is fitted with spheres slewed $15\frac{1}{2}°$ from the athwartship line, starboard sphere forward. When alongside a wharf and heading 030° C the spheres were correcting a deviation of 4° E.

Later the ship was swung with the spheres in place and the following deviations observed:

Ship's head by Compass	N	NE	E	SE	S	SW	W	NW
Deviation		6° E	3° E	3° W	8° W	3° W	1° W	2° E	4° E

How should the spheres be placed to correct for quadrantal deviation?

Answer. The spheres are placed to correct a $-E$ and a $+D$ and numerically $\dfrac{E}{D} = \tan(2 \times 15\frac{1}{2}°) = \tan 31° = 0{\cdot}6.$

$$\therefore E = 0{\cdot}6D \quad \text{and} \quad -E + 0{\cdot}6D = 0.$$

The spheres were *correcting* $+4°$ when heading 030° C.

$$\therefore -E\cos 60 + D\sin 60 = 4$$
$$-0{\cdot}5E + 0{\cdot}866D = 4$$

and
$$-0{\cdot}5E + 0{\cdot}3D = 0$$

subtracting
$$0{\cdot}566D = 4$$

$$D = \frac{4}{0{\cdot}566} = +7$$

$$E = 7 \times 0{\cdot}6 = -4{\cdot}2.$$

From analysis we get $\quad E = \dfrac{+6 + 3 - 3 - 2}{4} = +1$

$$D = \frac{+3 + 8 - 1 - 4}{4} = +1{\cdot}5.$$

The spheres are correcting a $-4{\cdot}2E$ and a $+7{\cdot}0D$.

The analysis shows a $+1{\cdot}0E$ and a $+1{\cdot}5D$.

Coefficients due to ship are $-3{\cdot}2E$ and $+8{\cdot}5D$.

The spheres must therefore be re-slewed.

For new angle of slew

$$\text{Tan } 2M = \frac{E}{D} = \frac{3\cdot2}{8\cdot5}$$
$$2M = 20\cdot6°$$
$$M = 10\cdot3°.$$

The spheres should be slewed 10° from the athwartship line, starboard sphere forward.

Maximum deviation to be corrected

$$= \sqrt{E^2 + D^2}$$
$$= \sqrt{3\cdot2^2 + 8\cdot5^2}$$
$$= 9\cdot1°.$$

INDEX